Passwords for All Seasons

Passwords
for All Seasons

By
Dick Gray

Foreword by Sigurd F. Olson

Freshwater Biological Research Foundation
Minneapolis

THIS BOOK IS PRINTED ON 100 PERCENT RECYCLED PAPER.

DEDICATED TO

Those hundreds — if not thousands — of early believers in the concept of the Freshwater Biological Institute, whose moral and financial support helped make a dream become a reality.

Foreword

Passwords for All Seasons is an unusual book written by an unusual man whose far-ranging curiosity regarding all aspects of his immediate world and his relationship to it dominates his thinking. Richard Gray has culled from his Sun Newspaper column "Pass-Words" a multiplicity of fascinating subjects, bringing them together in a beautiful book many thousands will treasure. With few attempts to revise and polish, they are as fresh as the day they were conceived.

While these essays cover many diverse ideas and thoughts, inevitably they are based on the overall concept that man is a part of nature and its life and that the reason for our treatment of the earth, the exhaustion of natural resources, and pollution of air, soil, and water, and growing ugliness is due to ignorance and lack of understanding. This he sees everywhere about him, recognizing that if man is to survive and live richly and fully, he must work with nature rather than against it.

As he wrote me recently, "If only more people could accept the time span of the geologist and realize the impact of massive ecological ebbs and flows spread over great lengths of time; if only more people would become less concerned with just themselves and more concerned about others and the life about them, they would be happier and the earth a better place in which to live."

As a former geologist and paleobotanist, he has this long point of view which gives perspective and depth to all he writes and insight into his concerns. As an industrialist in our technological system, he knows intuitively that the quality of life is more important than quantity and the accumulation of wealth for its own sake, and that there must be a balance between industrial use and nature if a state of equilibrium and harmony is to be achieved.

He also knows we must use our vast knowledge to right the wrongs of the past and work toward the preservation of the earth rather than its further degradation. He believes we must start somewhere with meaningful activity preserving places of beauty near our homes. For him this means Lake Minnetonka and his home at the Pass.

His busy life on this still lovely lake, his consciousness of its problems, his mounting concern over its growing pollution, has not diminished his joy in its wonders or his constant exploration of its waters and shorelines. Not a day passes but he finds something to marvel at, some hidden secret to challenge his probing natural curiosity. His questioning is boundless, his excitement contagious, and as we travel with him on his many expeditions of discovery in *Passwords,* we too become excited over what he finds to share with us. He is truly spurred and inspired by the power of wonder.

While he has traveled widely, to him there is no place in the world better than Lake Minnetonka, and it was natural he should be saddened by its present plight of pollution, inadequate zoning, and the spreading blight of suburban developments. With little being done to help restore the lake to what it used to be, or at least to maintain it as it was only yesterday with wise management and control, the problem was constantly with him. As time went by and he watched conditions getting worse and worse, his dream of restoration became an all-absorbing goal to somehow bring the lake back to at least a semblance of its former purity. He knew it would take a great deal of money and all the expertise that could be mustered to bring about a solution. Questioning, personal study, and observation ensued, then at last the dream in the grand concept of the Freshwater Biological Institute, an effort into which during the past five years he has poured his time and his energy. He talked first to friends and neighbors as concerned as he, especially Hibbert Hill, Carroll Crawford, and Dr. Alan Brook, then to the University of Minnesota's President Malcolm Moos, the Dean of the College of Biological Sciences, Richard S. Caldecott, and the Board of Regents, to the heads of foundations, corporations, local, state, and federal agencies, to aquatic biologists, ecologists and conservationists, and found everywhere understanding and support. It would take, he soon found out, several million dollars to build the Institute even on donated land, but he was not deterred, and embarked on a program that would have made most men quail before its enormity.

As he stated in his first descriptive brochure, "For years there have been many resource studies of fresh water contamination here and abroad, but in the United States not one central body where basic fresh water research could be coordinated. The goal of the Institute is to provide the facilities, equipment, and intelligence for a broad frontal coordinated attack against the almost limitless and complex problems of fresh water, learn the answers to these complexities and then apply them to fresh water needs here on Lake Minnetonka, around the nation, and perhaps the world."

To enumerate the many generous donors, individuals, organizations and corporations who realized the soundness and originality of the approach would be difficult. The simple facts emerge that by the end of 1973, the goal of raising four million dollars was all but realized, the building on Lake Minnetonka was essentially completed, a director had been appointed, a competent staff was in the process of being assembled, and the Institute had the complete acceptance of the College of Biological Sciences of the University of Minnesota.

As Dean Richard S. Caldecott said, "It is a fitting tribute to Minnesotans that they started the Freshwater Biological Institute and structured it in such a way that through time it will remain an invaluable resource for all mankind."

No one man could accomplish what has been done alone, but the dream and original inspiration was Richard Gray's, and by seeing it through to completion he set a pattern for lakes and streams everywhere. The great idea came fortunately at a time of national and growing concern for our environment when people were ready and willing to accept and endorse it. Their wholehearted and sympathetic response to his appeal for help proved they were ready to work and to give to make the dream come true.

"The Institute," as he told me recently, "has created a unique melding of the business and academic worlds working together toward a common goal. It has caught the fancy of young and old and one of its results will be the intermixing of the layman with and within a great scientific endeavor. Certainly its approach using the modern multi-diciplinary concept sets it apart from other enterprises in the world of freshwater biology." In the opinion of internationally known candidates for Director, "The Freshwater Biological Institute stands alone."

This book, *Pass-Words for All Seasons,* is not about the Institute or the coordinated effort that went into its successful creation, but rather about many things Richard Gray has seen in his daily roaming around the countryside or over the lake itself. It should be of tremendous interest to everyone for it reflects his love of the environment with an awareness always of man's total relationship to the earth. There is a constant excitement about his discoveries and how he sees things and what he thinks about.

The eighty essays grouped in a seasonal pattern give it special interest and timeliness. Enhanced by the sketches of Dr. Walter Breckenridge and line drawings by Daniel Metz, it is a beautiful and significant book. It cannot help but make us more conscious of our natural heritage and perhaps more alive to what is around us. Anyone reading these selected essays will look at his surroundings with new understanding and delight.

SIGURD F. OLSON
Ely, Minnesota

Preface

The publisher and recipient of all proceeds from the sale of this book is the Freshwater Biological Research Foundation, a non-private Minnesota foundation, that was formed for the express purpose of siring the Freshwater Biological Institute and giving it, with equipment and operating funds, to the University of Minnesota as an outright gift from all of us. Your purchase of *Passwords for All Seasons* has helped, in part, to fund the project.

This book is a collection of 80 "Pass-Words" columns selected from some 260 written during the five-year period 1968 through 1972. They were weekly grist fed into the public mill via the Sun Newspapers. Although originally intended for a fairly local audience in the greater Lake Minnetonka area, they became a popular choice for "wheeling" or optional use by all of the 26-odd editions of the Sun Newspapers in the greater Metropolitan Twin City region.

The column is called "Pass-Words" for three main reasons: I live on a strip of land between two main bodies of water in the western section of Lake Minnetonka, which strip has been traditionally called the "Pass" (and was one of the best duck-shooting spots in Minnesota in the old days); the intent of the column was to put into words my observations, experiences, and the resulting philosophies of living on the Pass; and hopefully, the style of and information in the columns would help others to some passwords and door-openers to the Natural World about us.

"Pass-Words" has been an enjoyable hobby for me — a hobby because the columns have been supplied the Sun Newspapers without monetary compensation to me. In no way do I pretend to be either a professional writer or a professional scientist. I may know a little about a lot of things, but I'm the first to admit there's nothing about which I even begin to know everything.

I have always been fascinated by the mysteries and functions of all things about us and consider myself fortunate to have the classroom and field training of a petroleum geologist with associated work in botany, zoology, and both organic and inorganic chemistry. My business life has revolved around engineering, manufacturing, and sales, and a far-flung organization has given me the opportunity to travel to most parts of the world. Two years of Naval duty plying the Pacific Ocean during WW II added experiences onto experiences.

It is especially true in my case that one doing research and writing is indebted to the intelligence, perseverence, and documentation of countless past and present people who cared to investigate and record the fruits of their investigations in the form of books, periodicals, pictures, and drawings. I wish to give blanket credit to each individually and everybody collectively for the data made available for me to peruse and incorporate in the columns.

It's been amazing to me, however, the number of discrepancies in factual data that exist from one reliable source to another. If there are any inaccuracies in material in a column, I certainly apologize, but I believe I have attempted to be accurate, or at the very least to present the viewpoint of the majority of the sources. Also, if an explanation or a point seems somewhat incomplete, again I apologize but hasten to explain that the limitation of approximately one thousand words per newspaper column oftentimes necessitates an abbreviated discourse.

The Sun organization has given permission for all of these columns to be reprinted in book form for the benefit of the Freshwater Biological Institute. I give special thanks to Mr. Sigurd Olson who, with his wife, served hot, fresh wild blueberry pie to my wife and me during a planning session at his home in Ely, Minnesota, and who so kindly contributed the Foreword to this book. Dr. Walter Breckenridge, former head of the Museum of Natural History of the University of Minnesota, has generously consented to the use of four of his pen and inks, which drawings were done in 1937 and 1938 for a limited edition of bird pictures for Dr. Thomas Roberts. The University of Minnesota Press has granted permission for their use.

The fifteen original pen and ink drawings by Mr. Daniel Metz are deserving of special note. Dan is only twenty-one years old, lives with his mother, father, and ten brothers and sisters on a farm in Delano, Minnesota, has never had a formal art lesson, and has done these drawings as his contribution to the Freshwater Biological Institute. I'm especially pleased to think that this book might be of help in launching the career of a young artist.

Initial encouragement to write a weekly column came from Mr. James Williams and Mr. Hibbert Hill, for which I thank them. It is my wife Kay, however, who has had to bear the brunt of the pangs of column-birth week after week after week. She also gave her time and interest to the editing and selecting of the columns for this book. I give her my thanks, appreciation, and apologies for those disruptions in our lives that have occurred because of "Pass-Words."

I am grateful to Mr. Les Blacklock for the use of the beautiful color photograph on the front of the jacket, and to Mr. Les Kouba for the painting he did for the Telethon for Freshwater in 1972, which he donated to the Freshwater Biological Institute, shown in black and white on the back of the jacket. Among the many other people involved with this book, I especially wish to thank Mr. John Kopacek for his line drawings and graphs, Mr. Henning Jensen for his sensitive book design, and the staff of Dillon Press for their patient assistance to an amateur author.

For me, the creation of "Pass-Words" and the incorporation of some of them into this book has been total pleasure. I trust the reader will enjoy them. We do live in a magnificent biosphere where bottomless cups of wonders can never be drained. Fortunate are we that we can sup at this cup, thereby enriching our own lives.

Passwords for All Seasons

Part 1

THE WINTER SEASON
December through February

*"...a gorgeous lake...a totally usable lake
...a visiting spot for presidents of the
United States...."*

MAKE MINE MINNETONKA

One night not too long ago, my wife and I were drinking in the deep beauty of a full moon shining on our wonderful lake, the wide beam of white light sparkling and shimmering over a mild riffle. Both of us agreed that if we were watching such a scene someplace else in the world, we would never forget it and would recall it time and again as a high spot of one of our numerous trips.

We reminisced over some of the many moon occasions remembered from our travels:

The peace of a full moon over the Mediterranean on an Easter Eve, rising in back of and over the glittering gold mosaic duomo of the main church in Positano, Italy, while a snaking, candlelight procession threaded its way down a narrow path and into the dark church. The yellowness radiating from the candles flowed through one of the windows of the church and matched the softness of the reflected light from our earth's only satellite.

The sharpness of the bright white night light under a Vermont moon that seeped through partially drawn drapes while we relaxed in front of a crackling fire in a rustic lodge deep in the high rolling hills after a fine day of skiing at Stowe.

The mellowness of a soft yellow full moon as it climbed out of the deep blue water of the Caribbean at Grand Cayman Island in the West Indies, climaxing a brilliant day that included fighting and landing two 45-pound Wahoos from a small 16-foot rowboat in the choppy open sea.

A full moon is magnificent no matter where it's seen, but moon moments on Lake Minnetonka are especially beautiful because they happen at home. A mellow moon on Minnetonka, however, is only a small part of the love for that lake that goes ever so deeply.

As a boy, I spent my summers growing up at Farm Island Lake between Mille Lacs Lake and Aitkin, Minnesota. Minnetonka was unknown to me, even though I had lived most of my life, until then, in nearby Minneapolis. I have visited, fished, and hunted innumerable lakes and rivers over the years throughout the world and I love them all with the special beauties that each of them possesses.

As nice as all of those other places have been, however, none can approach Minnetonka for all-round greatness, in my opinion.

Where else can you find a gorgeous lake so near a major city, a lake that is known for its beauty and can be enjoyed by thousands within minutes from their homes, instead of being tucked away and unavailable to all but a few because of an isolated location? Where else is there a totally usable boating lake with more than a hundred miles of interesting shoreline encompassing some of the best fishing in the world, a lake full of islands and bays, channels and long open reaches, a lake that teems with the activities of cruisers, rowboats, pontoon boats, swimmers, sailboats, speedboats, skin divers, water skiers, iceboats, skate sailers, snowmobiles, skaters, fish houses, fishermen, cars, and even motorcycles slewing over the ice and snow?

Here is a lake that has been a major recreational area for literally millions of people since its discovery by the white man in 1822, a short three years after Fort Snelling on the Mississippi River was established. A visiting spot for presidents of the United States, a raceway for smoke-belching paddlewheelers, a happy hunting grounds for Indians whose past is documented by the numbers of burial mounds near and on its shores, Minnetonka has a rich, teeming history that defies a simple summation.

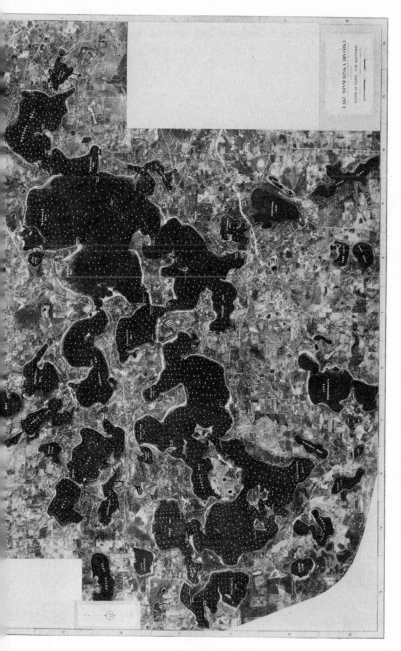

First aerial photo of Lake Minnetonka, May 15, 1934. Lake level is 5.2 feet below the 929.4 foot crest of Grays Bay Dam because of drought. Courtesy of Mark Hurd Aerial Surveys, Inc.

5

It has played hostess to the famous and the unknown, to the local as well as the most distant foreigner. It has seen the violence of death through drownings, tornadoes, boat collisions, and electrocutions. It has lived through the passing of generations of lake lovers whose children have carried forward the special feeling of those who know and cherish our lovely lake.

Minnetonka has been a mother to the multitudes.

And yet, night after night in the heart of summer, we have been boating under a billion stars without meeting a soul, savoring the lake all to ourselves with only an occasional falling star to add visible motion to the blanket of deep blue overhead and a barking dog somewhere in the distance to create a slight ripple in the stillness of a superb night.

Who can top the thrill of watching dozens of white and gaily colored sails during the races of both the Upper and Lower Lake yacht clubs — or the cozy throbbing of an idling boat engine somewhere out there in the dark — or the delicate but dramatic pink of a sunrise on the shining mirror-ice of the freshly frozen lake?

For me, the other wonders of the world are fine places to visit, but I wouldn't trade them as places to live. Give me the special wonder that is at our front and back doors, that wonder so thoroughly enjoyed by those who know it, but which is still such a mystery to most of the people in our Twin City area.

For my money, make mine Minnetonka.

January, 1968

*"The lake had frozen in front of my eyes
...with clusters of surface frost crystals
making like a solid field of diamonds."*

WATCHING THE LAKE FREEZE

It was simply beautiful Sunday morning as the sun came up. The air was clear, the temperature about zero, and after so many days of no sun, it was a most welcome sight to watch the sun rise so far to the south over Crane Island. At least half of the Upper Lake in front of the Pass was still open water; waving wisps of steam caught the pink of the rising sun and passed the delicate shades from one to another. Along the edge of some of the ice closer to shore, a few mallards and golden eyes played.

This was at about a quarter to eight in the morning. By nine o'clock the ducks were gone, the sun was up, the steam only short little streamers, and in the telescope the open water surface looked stiff, as if it were fresh taffy. By ten o'clock a couple of ducks were back, but this time they had landed and were sitting on ice — ice that was absolutely brand new. The lake had frozen in front of my eyes and the new ice was sparkling with clusters of surface frost crystals making like a solid field of diamonds.

Water is a strange mixed-up thing, yet so essential to everything. It is the only chemical that occurs in our everyday life as a liquid, a solid, and as a gas. It is a universal solvent, stores tremendous amounts of heat to keep our climates balanced, cools our bodies through perspiration, and maintains our body heat by a thin layer of moisture which insulates our skin against sudden temperature changes.

We take water for granted most of the time, but try this out for size: There are 33 different chemical kinds of water which, in the main, all revolve around the properties of hydrogen and oxygen. Besides our common water, so-called heavy water is the next most common. Hydrogen has two big brothers (called isotopes) that also love oxygen. One is twice as heavy as hydrogen and is called deuterium. The other is three times as heavy and is called tritium. The latter joins with oxygen to form T_2O; the former becomes D_2O or heavy water. It boils at 214 ½ degrees Farenheit and freezes at 38 7/8 degrees. Physiologically we can't use it.

When two or more atoms of a basic element get together, a compound is formed. There are two common ways that atoms join together. The first is by ionic bonding, where an atom (like chlorine) is looking for one more charged electron in its structure, and another atom (like sodium) has an extra one to share with somebody. The result is a happy marriage of the have and have-not. In this instance, we get common table salt or sodium chloride.

The other way atoms join is by covalent bonding, where different atoms share electrons between them. Common water is an example, and the water molecule so formed by two atoms of hydrogen and one atom of oxygen (H_2O) is called a polar molecule, because it has a north and south pole. The attraction of the poles causes the hydrogen atoms to be hooked onto the oxygen atom exactly 105 degrees apart — making a configuration much like Mickey Mouse with his big ears.

It so happens that hydrogen atoms like each other, so water has the many properties of its molecules staying together, with high surface tensions (like floating a pin in a glass of water) or water coating a rock. As water cools, its molecules keep rearranging themselves in respect to each other, getting more compact and cozy until 39.2 degrees Farenheit is reached — the point of maximum density and therefore the point at which water is heaviest. Then, as the temperature gets even cooler, water keeps rearranging its

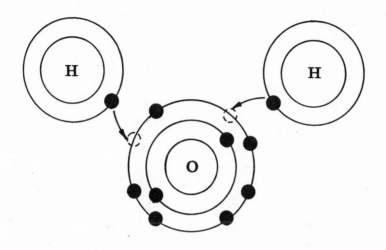

TWO H PLUS O EQUAL H_2O OR WATER
With a Mickey Mouse Configuration

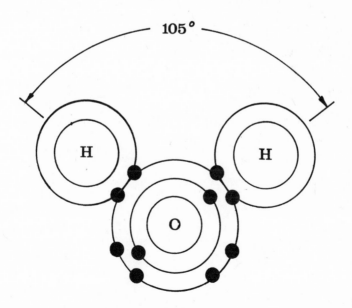

105°

molecules, but now the molecules become farther apart, less dense, and therefore lighter until 32 degrees or freezing is reached.

At this point (that which I watched Sunday morning) the molecules suddenly rearrange themselves in a definite hexagonal pattern with the molecules held together by the attraction of the hydrogens. The result is ice, and the hex or six-sided crystals formed are very apparent in the spring when the ice becomes honeycombed. At the time of freezing, the liquid water gives off heat and expands one ninth in volume, which is why things burst when becoming frozen. As ice gets colder, it contracts because the molecules get closer together, causing cracks to open up in the ice. As ice warms up, it expands, as the molecules become more active and move farther apart, causing ridges in the ice and heaving along the shore.

In the solidifying of water to make ice or in the solidifying of lava to make stone, the faster it happens the smaller are the crystals that make up the solid. The slower the water freezes, the larger are its crystals. Ice that is formed during calm air is nice and smooth; ice that is formed with some water movement going on is likely to be uneven. Some ice is made up of broken bits of skin ice or fairly thick chunks of ice that have broken up, washed up on shore and then refrozen into an uneven sheet.

The next time you casually look at ice, realize it's a changing thing with properties hard to believe. Let common water molecules decide *en masse* that they want to change their ways — and we've had it. Along with some other things, water is man's best friend, and I for one intend to treat it with respect.

December, 1971

"...he...swooped up the hapless duck
...and tore it apart. Life is so very fragile."

OUR NATIONAL EMBLEM

As I start to write, it's still dark outside this early morning with a slight hint of pink to the east, but something is happening that I've rarely experienced. Although the temperature is 32 degrees, the main Upper Lake pretty much froze over during the night, and is still continuing to freeze now. The fresh light east wind of about eight miles an hour is causing the entire ice sheet to undulate, as if the lake surface were covered by a thin plastic sheeting. A very peculiar tinkly crackling like the sound of some crazy sheet metal bells is filling the air as the tenuous ice film struggles to hold together.

Our visitors timed their arrival well. What visitors? Well, Friday morning early I was standing at our eastern windows watching the beautiful sight of the day brightening into view when the thousand or so ducks feeding along the shore got up *en masse.* I peered up and down the shoreline but saw no reason why they should leave — when suddenly the most stately, handsome, huge bald eagle coasted over our roof from the west and out above the Upper Lake. I rushed to my spotting scope and for many minutes followed him as he soared, flapped a couple of times, and then soared some more. Gradually, he worked his way to the north, over Hardscrabble Point, finally disappearing near Priest's and Cook's Bay areas which had frozen a couple of days before.

Over the weekend, I saw this white-headed eagle a couple more times, but I also saw two or three younger birds that must have arrived along with him but had not lived the necessary three or four years to fully develop the distinctive white head and tail. A one-year-old has a dark head, and a two-year-old a gray head. It was like seeing old friends to have them back, as they or other eagles have come to Minnetonka for many a year just as the lake is freezing. I checked back in my records and found that eagles showed up Dec. 2, 1966, Dec. 3, 1967, Dec. 7, 1968, Nov. 21, 1969, Dec. 4, 1970.

Eagles migrate but go only far enough south to escape the ice. They will stay around here as long as there is open water on the lake — usually over the deep spots in the main Upper and Lower lakes. I've watched them many a time walking along the edge of the water on the ice, carefully checking out the water's edge for fish and other matter that might have drifted against the ice. I've seen eagles perched high in trees along open streams near Aspen, Colorado, in the wintertime, and I'm sure many skiers have seen the eagles that hang around the Namekagon River near Telemark in Wisconsin the entire winter.

The other day I watched as a magnificent bald eagle landed on the ice not fifty feet from a dozen or so golden eyes paddling in a small opening in the ice. Every few seconds, the eagle would partly open his wings and waddle a few feet towards the ducks. From ten feet away, he finally took off and swooped up a hapless duck, landed, and tore it apart. I couldn't help but think — it took at least six or seven months for the duck to grow, and it was all over in a couple of minutes. Life is so very fragile.

We're privileged to have the scarce eagles stop off each fall. Fewer and fewer birds are reported each year. With all of the recent interest in man's environment and what we're doing to it, the eagle becomes even more important. Besides being our national emblem, it was also sacred to Zeus, god of the elements, and history records the eagle as being the symbol of power and beauty for the Romans, French, Mexicans, Greeks, Russians, Prussians, and Austri-

A Golden-Eye Meets an Eagle

ans. Even though Ben Franklin was pushing for the wild turkey to be our national bird, Congress decided upon the bald eagle in 1782. The bird is on the presidential seal and the "eagle" was a $10 gold coin weighing 258 grains that went out of service in 1934.

We have to be sure the bird itself doesn't go out of service. The bald eagle *(Haliaeetus leucocephalus)* is of the same family as hawks, vultures, ospreys, and kites. They keep the same mate for life and build huge nests. One such nest measured ten feet across by twenty feet deep and weighed a couple tons. Nests have been found to include such things as fish plugs, light bulbs, and even an old tablecloth. Babies are called eaglets, their home is an eyrie, and a nest with babies is a clutch. Roberts states in *Birds of Minnesota* that there was an eagle's nest on Minnetonka with two young observed in the nest June 30, 1874. Grown females are larger than the males, but mature birds will average seven to eight feet in wingspread, weigh eight to twelve pounds, and are from three to three and one-half feet long.

Perhaps it was an old female that glided over our house and frightened the ducks. Certainly the wingspread was the maximum, as it seemed well over twice the length of the body. Eagles will roam over all of Lake Minnetonka and to surrounding lakes like Christmas Lake as long as there is open water. They're a fine sight to see and in my opinion much more fitting to be our national emblem than the wild turkey. Sorry about that, Mr. Franklin.

November, 1969

*"In Basle, Santa Claus really comes, sometimes
on horseback dressed as a bishop who, along
with a servant, shows some children the strong
faith if they haven't been obedient."*

A SWISS CHRISTMAS

Tucked into the northwest corner of Switzerland, where
Germany, France, and Switzerland literally meet, is the city
of Basel (English) or Bale (French) or Basle (German). The
River Rhine serves as a water highway to the sea and has
made this city a strong commercial center for central
Europe. It is about as large as St. Paul but, strangely enough,
a city little known to Americans. I know it well, having
visited it many a time while transacting business there for
the past twenty-one years. While I cherish the memories
of many pleasant experiences, the friends I have made there
are what I value the most.

Basle (I prefer the German spelling because it's a German-
oriented city) is split into two cantons or political divisions,
and high on a hill in the suburb of Binnengin, in the rural
canton of Basle, sits a wonderful house with picture windows
allowing a sweeping view of the city. The warmth of the
family within the house makes it a home. You'll feel some
of that warmth coming through these words from a letter
I received from there. Conrad S. is the writer.

"Dick, before I describe what we do personally at Christmas, I would like to draw your attention to the variety of
forms in which Christmas is celebrated in Switzerland.
Practically each canton has its own traditions and this
varies through the whole season after Michael-mass in the

middle of the fall, as a last glance at the sunny period of summer is given. The winter starts with Martinmas in November when the harvest is done. Children go around the fields with lanterns, a little bit like at Hallowing-day." (Note: I suppose this is similar to our Halloween.)

"The real Christmas season starts with the first Advent. In many regions, people make a garland of fir branches and decorate it with four wax candles and light one as each of the four Sundays before Christmas arrives. On these Advent Sundays, we sit together with the children and sing Christmas carols and tell or read Christmas stories.

"An event which is more in the common social life is Santa Claus Day, December 5 or 6 (depending upon the Catholic or Protestant regions). In some parts of the country, especially the French-speaking, children put their boots under the chimney or in front of their room and find them the next day filled with cookies, apples, or some small presents. In Basle, Santa Claus really comes, sometimes on horseback dressed as a bishop who, along with a servant, shows some children the strong faith if they haven't been obedient. In the Canton of Zurich, there is a woman called the 'flour witch' who threatens to eat them if they're not obedient.

"The weeks following Santa Claus Day are full of preparations for Christmas presents. In these days, the presents are often bought, but they should not be, as the value is in what is done by the handcraft of the children. The week before Christmas is full of bakery flavour in our homes. We make different cookies, such as gingerbread, anise bread, cinnamon, hip, and poppy cookies, presented in forms of stars, moons, hearts, birds, Santa Clauses and so on.

"At Christmas, again, the customs vary as to the regions. There are groups of singers going around the town or the village. They receive from the population cookies or something to drink as rewards for the singing. One of the oldest singing customs is in Rheinfelder (near Basle), where a group of twelve men, called the Sebastian brothers, dress in black coats and cylinder hats while singing in the town. At 2300 Christmas Eve (11 p.m.) they leave their lighted lanterns

A Swiss/Basle canton flag over the Pass

on the alter of San Sebastian. The same singing and lantern-carrying around town occurs on Sylvester-day (New Year's Eve) and has been done this way since the year A.D. 427.

"In other parts, like Lucerne, they make Christmas plays just in front of the cathedral or churches. You often see special figures showing the whole Christmas story with the crib in the center. We have a small one under our Christmas tree. When our son Manfred was small, we kept a room closed for him and on Christmas Eve he heard a bell, showing him the Christ child had finished his work. The door was opened and we all entered the room, seeing the decorated Christmas tree with all the wax candles and with gifts under the tree.

"We then sit down, sing Christmas carols and play them in the way each can — Justina with her violin or flute, Manfred with his flute and this year probably with his guitar. Then, I tell the Christmas story and we look at the different presents which Manfred brings to each of the family. If we can, we go to midnight mass.

"On Christmas Day it is family day with friends and we

go regularly to look at Christmas plays at Manfred's school. After Christmas, we continue to be conscious as much as possible of the thirteen holy nights from Christmas to Epiphanias or Three Kings Day, January 6. This final day of the Christmas season brings us the guidance which is shown in the way of the three kings.

"I hope, Dick, this material is of interest to you and I am so happy to be in contact with you in thoughts while telling this."

Well, Conrad, I'm with you also in thoughts while I write this. I'm sitting not twenty feet from the shores of Lake Minnetonka, which you know from your visits here. The lake water is frozen, snow is on the ground and covers the ice, but if the warmth of our friendship and understanding could be fully utilized, it would melt all that ice and snow. But that would be unseasonal. Instead, I direct all of that warmth into a Merry Christmas and a Happy New Year from all of us to all of you and may peace prevail with goodwill amongst all men.

December, 1971

*"...the Tamarack or American Larch drops its
needles each fall, whereas our pines, firs,
spruces, and cedars hold their needles."*

YOU CAN TELL BY THE NEEDLES

On Thanksgiving morning, an ad in the *Miami Herald*
proclaimed with bold letters,   "POLYVINYL CHLORIDE
SCOTCH PINE 6-FOOT TREES WITH 81 BRANCH TIPS
ONLY $9.97."

Now, how about that?! "Instant Christmas" for the thousands of condominium units! No needles to drop on synthetic
rugs, no danger of breakage to the dully colored plastic balls
dangling from the eighty-one ersatz branch tips, no water to
spill or pan to fill beneath the "tree." But then, everything
has its place, I guess, including artificial trees.

We have a small fake cedar tree on our office coffee table
at Christmas-time, and several apartment-dwelling friends
have had small plastic trees gaily decorated during the
holiday season. They're easy to store the rest of the year,
but maybe that Miami ad got to me because the sellers of
the fake 6-foot tall tree had the audacity to call it a Scotch
Pine.

Three days later the same Florida paper carried a news
article that stated the age of bristlecone pines near Elko,
Nevada to be 5,000 years, and said an expedition was on its
way to Wheeler Peak to locate a tree of the same species
supposed to be over 7,000 years old and still living. They
will tell its age by growth rings and carbon-dating of the
dead wood.

What a range of human interest — from a natural tree that sprouted possibly 5,000 years before Christ to a tree that quickly sprung from between two steel dies and whose seed was a handful of plastic pellets.

Evergreens, the holiday season, and Minnesota winters all go together, in my opinion. The dark glossy green of the Austrian pines against the white snow, the sighing of the wind as it passes through the cedar boughs, and the blobs of color from the strings of lights laced over and around the arms of a spreading spruce blend into a feeling of contentment that is ours to enjoy.

In our area, all evergreens are conifers, but all conifers aren't evergreens — see? A conifer is a tree that bears cones to carry the seeds. One of our conifers — the Tamarack or American Larch — drops its needles each fall, whereas our pines, firs, spruces, and cedars hold their needles. The other day I walked around our property, cut samples of branches, picked off cones from different conifers, and tried to identify them. Well, the job is tough because so many of our evergreens have been imported or are specially developed by nursery men.

PINE   SPRUCE

Because almost everybody deals with evergreens from time to time — for planting, for Christmas, for decorating — I put the following outline together to try to simplify what can be very confusing. This list applies to our immediate area.

Conifers: Mostly evergreen, leaves are needles or scales, and seeds come in woody cones.

1) Pines — needles are in bundles.
   a. White Pine *(Pinus strobus)* — only tree with five needles per bunch.
   b. Red or Norway Pine *(Pinus resinosa)* — two needles per bundle. Bark plate-like and reddish.
   c. Scotch Pine *(Pinus sylvestis)* — two needles per bundle, orange branches and scaly bark.
   d. Austrian Pine *(Pinus nigra)* — two needles per bundle — dark green, bushy branches.
   e. Tamarack or American Larch *(Larix laricina)* — can have many needles per bundle, drops them each fall.
2) Firs — needles are flat, occur singly.
   a. Balsam Fir *(Abies balsamea)* — bark gum is good to chew.

FIR   CEDAR

3) Spruces — needles are four-sided, occur singly.
    a. White Spruce *(Picea glanca)* — pretty cones one inch to two inches long. I would put the green and Colorado blue spruces in this category.
    b. Norway Spruce *(Picea abies)* — dark needles, six-inch cones, droopy branches.
4) Cedars and Junipers
    a. Northern White Cedar — flat scaly needles along branches.
    b. Red Cedar — scaly branches, prickly needles opposite each other.
    c. Dwarf Juniper — low, red, cedar-like needles in whorls of three.

In two or three years we can expect to see a new type of tree coming on the market. It has been developed by the Institute of Forest Genetics in California and is a cross between a chunky shore pine and a slim lodgepole pine. I haven't seen one but it is claimed this tree has lots of branches, is symmetrical, fast-growing, and an added attraction is gobs of small brown cones at the ends of the branches. Whether or not this tree is suitable for growth in Minnesota is open to question. If not, then we won't have a chance to buy them unless willing to pay a high premium for the long-distance shipping.

If new trees are placed onto the market, I'm all for the real ones instead of the fake ones. Plastic has its place — but I can't quite see decking the halls with boughs of polyvinyl chloride.

November, 1969

"...with a landing net, a stepladder,
help from a friend, and forty-five minutes,
...I deposited it in my greenhouse.
Both the bird and I were happy about it."

AN UNEXPECTED GIFT

Some Christmas presents come early, not to be opened until December 25. One of my presents came last weekend, ignoring the rail strike because it came under its own power, not requiring unwrapping because its package was natural, open to enjoy before Christmas Day.

I was stringing some colored lights on an outside spruce when a beautiful dove fluttered across the tennis court fence and landed in a crabapple tree still festooned with little dried fruit. To a certain extent, this bird was a friend of mine. I had talked it into my hand about two months before while it sat on a bush next to the duck corn feeder, sort of a bystander as the ducks ebbed and flowed. Upon catching the dove that first time, I carefully released it, after carrying it into the house to show it off. I hadn't seen it again until now.

Obviously it was a domesticated bird, probably a pet on the loose. This time I decided it couldn't survive our coming severe weather (20 below was the forecast for the night), so with a landing net, a stepladder, help from a friend, and forty-five minutes of time, I scooped up the lovely thing and deposited it in my greenhouse. Both the bird and I were happy about it.

It cooed a few times, and in a matter of hours was friendly to the point that it would climb onto my hand, walk up and down my arm, and loved being stroked across the back.

It was a gorgeous creature, about twelve inches long, smooth and sleek when not relaxed, fluffy and rumpled when relaxed. Its color is hard to describe; it was subtle, like a chocolate shake, very light on the chocolate. Its eyes were red and beady, its beak black, slightly curved, and an inch long, its feet and legs reddish with surprisingly long toenails. The only real marking on the entire body was a jet-black ring around its neck but open at the throat like a horseshoe.

Doves and pigeons are one and the same thing. Our common "downtown" pigeons are infinite varieties of the blue rock dove. They all belong to the family Columbidae and the only existing wild dove in the United States is the mourning dove. The two turtledoves of partridge-tree fame are the European counterparts of the mourning dove.

There have been some very famous doves. The long-extinct dodo bird was a distant relative, but we can hardly count that. One we can and should count, however, is the passenger pigeon. This famous bird was last seen in Minnesota in 1895 and the actual nest on display in the Museum of Natural History at the University of Minnesota was taken from the Minneapolis area September 6, 1874 — with a fresh egg still in the nest. The final wild passenger pigeon was seen in Connecticut in 1906 and the very last bird died in captivity in Cincinnati in 1914 at the age of 29. It's appalling that a bird whose flocks numbered in the billions should have been exterminated by man — but it was.

Other famous doves include the two doves that Noah released from the ark to check on the water level. Maybe I can train my newfound friend to do likewise this winter and save me those cold journeys onto the ice.

It's fun to observe a new thing at close range. My new dove — called a diamond dove by a pet store — can turn its head about 170 degrees on both sides of center, and has very dense plumage that can be easily pulled away from the body. There are four toes, but the three main ones point to the front and the back one seems so weak that it's hard for the bird to sit comfortably on a finger without tending to fall backwards.

Diamond Dove on Honduras Fern Post in Greenhouse

The only drawback to having the dove in my greenhouse to date is that the darned thing loves red begonia blossoms and has nearly stripped a new, $10 hanging basket from Bachman's.

Doves and pigeons drink in a manner different from other birds. Usually, a bird fills its bill with water and then lifts its head for the water to run down its throat. Doves, however, stick their beaks into the water up to their nostrils and suck to their hearts' content. I can't find out why this is. Young doves and pigeons survive on "pigeon's milk," which they siphon from the mother's mouth. This "gook" is very thin food prepared in the mother's crop and coughed up at mealtime. As the kids grow older, the soup gets thicker until they become smart enough to pass the stuff by.

As we grow older, maybe there will also be some things we can't stomach any longer. Like not having peace — or not containing our population growth — or not being super-careful about the preservation of endangered species. These are "3 P's" that tie in directly to the doves and pigeons: the dove of peace with an olive sprig in its mouth; the population explosion of the passenger pigeon into so many billions that one flock could eat more than 17 million baskets of grain from a field in one day; and the total extermination of those billions of birds, from countless numbers to none left to preserve.

If we could solve the problems relating to those 3 P's, what a Christmas present that would be. No need for presents other than that.

December, 1970

*"The more that is shared and given, the more
is received — and that keeps the circle circling
so you want to give even more."*

WHO GIVES WHAT?

More and more each year, Christmas cards are swinging.
The sentiments are still there, in the main, but the art work
and the ways of expressing Christmas joy keep changing.
Years ago I saw a far-out Christmas card that has stuck in
my mind, not only because of the graphic presentation of
its idea but because of the sentiment about Christmas that
it expressed. It was way ahead of its time.

As I remember it, the plain white card had a grinning
bright red devil on it — forked tail and all — with his hand
out. On opening the card, the message inside read, "Gimme
— the Christmas Spirit."

Now, there are several ways to react to that statement,
but it brought to my mind the old saying, "It's better to give
than to receive." Give what? Who gives what?

I believe that Giving IS Receiving.

I believe that Receiving IS Giving.

I believe that the whole ball game revolves around the
spirit of communication. To take communion, to live in a
commune, to be communicable, to be a communicant, to
commute — all of these words not only imply but actually
encompass the passage of ideas and feelings and love and
togetherness which is what the spirit of Christmas should
embrace.

There are so many representative words that can express

this business of giving and receiving. Of all of the words, "words" itself is that thing that applies to man and only man. Here is the priceless thing that we have, the ability to speak to each other, that totally unique vehicle that allows for communication at the highest level. And yet I don't believe any of us take total advantage of this gift. I know I don't. We just don't level with each other and thereby aren't leveling with ourselves. If all of us could give freely through our ability to impart words, what we would receive back would be an interchange with other people who would give because they were receiving.

Individual words can represent giving and receiving. How about "looks"? You know darn well that giving is receiving. Give a dirty look and, boy, more often than not you get one right back. Give a look of love and — pow!! — "he scores!!" per Al Shaver. Try looking at the beautiful sunrise — the joy and contentment you will feel is something you don't receive without the looking. Be willing to give by looking, and you reap the harvests of reciprocation.

How about "feelings"? Not only feelings, but the act of feeling, too. If you can let yourself go and give yourself the chance to stroke soft skin or fur, or rub coarse bark — let people know when they hurt you or when they please you — the satisfaction returned to you is the receiving because of the giving.

And how about "thoughts"? Well, you only get what you're willing to give. Who knows about another's thoughts except through what a person does or says — or how an animal reacts or doesn't — this must be an outward manifestation of what goes on inside. A jumbled bunch of values or a kindness to one and all — both must be expressions of thoughts dictated by the heart. The more that is shared and given, the more is received — and that keeps the circle circling so you want to give even more.

Compassion, love, understanding, humility, intelligence — all are words expressing feelings and happenings so important for a constant interchange between people and people, people and other living things, people and inanimate nature. I think it's impossible to give these things to others without receiving back a whole load of good things. It is impossible to receive these things from others without wanting to give even more right back. What a two-way street, what a back-to-back way of pyramiding your attributes, what a beautiful series of ways of expressing what the Christmas spirit is all about.

But then, there are things that happen to sorely try the Christmas spirit. I gave one of my sons a small spruce to plant in his front yard, a spruce I was fond of, having raised it from a seedling. The tree prospered until the other night, when an unknown, making large footprints in the snow, cut the tree in two and left the top lying there — mute but loud evidence of the meanness of one person. But then, the monkey must be on his back. He's the one who has the problem, he's the one who must live with a soul that would do such a thing, he's the one who sneaks and destroys and must be all twisted up inside. I wonder what he would do if he received the kind of thing that he gave....

It accomplishes nothing to dwell on the bad when there's so much good around. Friends and family, beauty and living, the press of a tiny hand from a contented grandchild, the stillness of an early morn — things that give in a constant flow for all of us to pass on for others to receive.

May you have a most happy holiday season by both giving and receiving.

December, 1972

"...the average person exudes about 1 ½ pints of water in 12 hours, and this moisture enters his clothing....damp clothing is cold clothing."

WARM THOUGHTS

Years ago during a routine physical examination, my doctor told me that I burn up more "fuel" just sitting quietly in a chair than most people do running down the street. This explains why I can eat three big meals a day, snack whenever I want to, and still never worry about my weight. I have a high metabolism rate.

I bring this up merely to show that no two people are exactly alike and, when discussing how to keep warm outside in our winter weather, only general statements can be made, because the elements and our reactions to them are a very individual thing. I create a lot of heat because of my metabolism. Some people don't.

Our Minnesota winters can become a matter of life or death to any one of us at any time. Dressing properly when outdoors, according to the prevailing circumstances, makes sense. It also makes it more fun to be outside. If you can, you might as well be comfortable. But it's the emergencies that could get us. All of us should keep extra clothing, boots, and mittens in our cars (I don't do it). Who knows when a long walk from a stuck car might become a necessity and a real trial?

A low temperature can be distressing, but the addition of a wind to the low temperature compounds the problem. Wind-chill charts have been printed and talked about, and

I think they're very important. The table here is a special one because it's simplified. I see no reason to chart temperatures warmer than 30 above or colder than 30 below on the thermometer. I see no reason to chart winds stronger than 30 m.p.h. If the wind is more than that and the temperature is way below zero, it's best to stay indoors!

To use this simplified chart, take the thermometer reading, find out the wind velocity, and where the two come together on the chart is the wind-chill factor. Two or three things are quite obvious. If the wind is stronger than 15 m.p.h., almost all temperatures less than 30 above result in below-zero wind-chills. So, strong winds mean dress as if it's way below zero outside.

Also, note that at all thermometer readings on the chart, the greatest wind-chill differences occur when the winds are between 5 and 15 m.p.h. At any given temperature, the average drop in wind-chill degrees is 16.4 degrees when the wind increases from 5 m.p.h. to 10 m.p.h. The average drop in degrees when the wind rises from 10 m.p.h. to 15 m.p.h. is 11.7 degrees. Say it's zero outside with a light 5 m.p.h. wind. Suddenly the wind kicks up to 15 m.p.h. Instead of a wind-chill of 6 below it suddenly is 33 degrees below zero and you have problems.

WIND-CHILL TABLE

WIND VELOCITY \ 0	THERMOMETER READING												
	30	25	20	15	10	5	0	-5	-10	-15	-20	-25	-30
5	27	21	16	12	7	1	-6	-11	-15	-20	-26	-31	-35
10	16	9	2	-2	-9	-15	-22	-27	-31	-38	-45	-52	-58
15	11	1	-6	-11	-18	-25	-33	-40	-45	-51	-60	-65	-70
20	3	-4	-9	-17	-24	-32	-40	-46	-52	-60	-68	-76	-81
25	0	-7	-15	-22	-29	-37	-45	-52	-58	-67	-75	-83	-89
30	-2	-11	-18	-26	-33	-41	-49	-56	-63	-70	-78	-87	-94

In Minnesota, we have occasional severe weather in the winter, and if we can't lick it, we might as well join it. The proper way to dress for cold weather is very important. Something that isn't generally taken into consideration is the fact that the average person exudes about 1 ½ pints of water every 12 hours, and this moisture enters his clothing. We all know that damp clothing is cold clothing, so Rule No. 1 is to wear the type of clothing that can absorb this moisture. It's one of the reasons why "waffle" underwear is so warm.

Our bodies make heat and, to stay warm in cold weather, we must retain as much heat as possible. Air is about the best type of insulation, so multiple layers of air is best. Dead air is most desirable. It so happens that "air" at any surface likes to stick to that surface and this stick-to-it-ness extends out about one-eighth of an inch from the surface. It also has been proven that, in general, almost any material is as warm as the next in relation to thickness (goose down is the best, however). So, the obvious conclusion is that several thin layers of almost any material is the best way to retain body heat. That's Rule No. 2.

Rule No. 3 is most important and simple: don't sweat. Sweating pumps more moisture into the clothing and uses up quantities of heat not only in the creation of sweat but also in the effort to evaporate the sweat. The "steady state" chart adapted and redrawn from *Snow Goer Magazine* clearly shows the drastic difference between thickness of insulation and types of activity. If more work is done, remove thickness as you warm up.

Here are some final statements modified from the same magazine:

1. Thickness is warmth, preferably in multiple layers.
2. A warm body will keep your fingers and toes warm.
3. Avoid sweating like the plague.
4. Use your head as a safety valve — keep it covered for warmth but uncover it to cool off.
5. Use an outer shell to keep out the wind and wet.
6. To create more heat, increase your metabolism by Indian wrestling with yourself. Muscular activity can in-

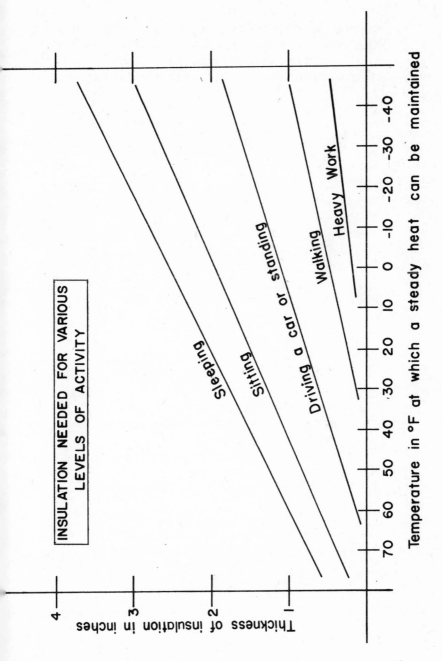

INSULATION NEEDED FOR VARIOUS LEVELS OF ACTIVITY

Sleeping

Sitting

Driving a car or standing

Walking

Heavy Work

Temperature in °F at which a steady heat can be maintained

Thickness of insulation in inches

33

crease your metabolism rate by as much as 750 percent.

When skiing or on a snowmobile or ice fishing — or walking from a stuck car in a wild blizzard — comfort is warmth and warmth is the result of being sensible. If you can, why not?

January, 1971

"The big breakthrough seems to have come around 1925 when [he]...took a toboggan and refashioned it by chopping a hole in the rear for a track."

THE AGE OF SNOWMOBILES

With startling speed, the snowmobile has become a major item on our winter scene. And, with equal speed, problems relating to their numbers and uses have arisen. It's just a matter of time before reasonable rules and regulations are put in effect, but until they are, the pros and cons of this newcomer will continue to be thrashed out.

Did I say newcomer? Well, hardly. I've had a snowmobile for many years, and I regard myself as one of the early owners around the lake. (Johnson-Evinrude made a few machines in 1965 and there were even some left unsold at the end of the season.) But if I rate myself as a "pioneer" user, then a recent article in *Snowgoer Magazine* puts me in my place.

The first United States patent for a "snow sled" was granted to three Runnoe brothers of Crested Butte, Colorado, March 24, 1896. A fellow up in Maine by the wonderful name of Alvin Orlando Lombard is said to have been the first to develop the concept of a continuous track for driving across snow. When Ford's Model T came on the scene in 1908, a Pine City, Minnesota, mechanic named Splittstoser (I hope he's careful when chopping wood) put a Ford on an old farm sled for winter travel. By the way, this gentleman is still alive at the age of 93 and lives in St. Paul.

In 1911, an Adel, Iowa, motorcyclist adapted his machine

for snow travel. Over the next few years, inventors from Hayward, Princeton, and Eland Junction, Wisconsin, tried their hands at perfecting good snow machines, essentially using automobiles with various runner and sled attachments. Admiral Byrd took a Model T with a track attachment to the Antarctic when Little America I was established, but the Ford never made it, as the track broke down only seventy-five miles from the starting point.

The big breakthrough seems to have come around 1925 when another Wisconsin inventor, Carl Eliason from Sayner, took a toboggan and refashioned it by chopping a hole in the rear for a track to be driven by an engine on the toboggan. He received a patent in 1927 and built forty machines which he sold for $360 each. At about this same time, a Canadian by the name of J. Armand Bombardier was busy perfecting a conveyor belt type of track. By 1930 he had it pretty well solved. Mr. Bombardier founded what is now the Bombardier Ski-Doo and is far and away the No. 1 snowmobile manufacturer in the world.

The period between 1930 and the early 1960s saw the development of air sleds for snow travel, the use of early snowmobile types in World War II, and the refinement of materials for bodies and tracks. Nobody is really clear as to why the snowmobile suddenly caught on in the '60s, but there's no question that it did. Probably the rise in our buying power, shorter work weeks, and the increase in leisure time — plus the rush to the rural areas for living — all contributed to the quick popularity of the machine.

If you have never been out for a snowmobile ride, you probably wonder what all the fuss and fascination is about. Besides being a reason to get outside during the winter, it's fun to just buzz around with a snowmobile. Lots of people put them to practical uses. I use mine to haul my power auger and sampling sled around Lake Minnetonka. Canadian guides who work for logging firms during the winter rent snowmobiles for $5 a day and up to four of them climb aboard and scoot home to the reservation for a weekend they couldn't have had without the snow machine. Trappers, resort owners, and ski-area operators,

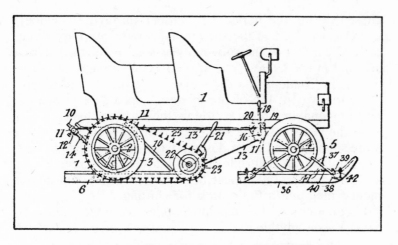

An early patent drawing of a snowmobile forerunner

to mention a few, regularly use the snowmobile.

There are snowmobile clubs, and a coming thing is to have very extensive snowmobile trails. Organized racing is now popular — even to the extent of racing on straw before the snow comes. The machine itself is growing up, too. Fancy dashboards with cigarette lighters, tachometers, gas gauges, speedometers, and odometers are common. Then add disc brakes, electric start, high- and low-beam dual headlights and twin tail lights, reverse transmission, colors and stripes on the steel and molded bodies, totally enclosed cabs, special snowmobile oil, plus fancy clothing and functional trailers.

It is estimated that by 1977 winter recreational vehicles will total $2 ½ billion in sales in the United States, and that by 1973 100,000 ATVs (all-terrain vehicles) will be produced, along with 1,000,000 snowmobiles. Today there are several dozen manufacturers of snowmobiles, but the number should drop to about 10 by the time the industry settles down to steady year-by-year production.

Some bits and pieces of industry information: There are now 11 European and at least one Japanese manufacturers of snowmobiles; 65 percent of the snowmobiles are purchased during the period of October through December; less than one-half of the snowmobiles purchased are financed; 70 percent of the snowmobiles sold in North America are sold in the United States; the largest foreign market to date is in Sweden; and the snowmobile has helped to preserve the way of life of the modern Laplanders in Scandinavia by enabling them to follow the reindeer herds.

As the years pass, the snowmobile will become more and more sophisticated in its design. Take the SSS (side-by-side snowmobile) by Evinrude. It has bucket seats, regular car steering, heater, radio, seat belts, twin-tracks, a full instrument panel, and a floor stick for shifting.

It's obvious. As far as snowmobiles are concerned, you haven't seen anything yet.

January, 1971

*"...they eat Japanese noodles which
means good luck, then they go to bed."*

NOODLES FOR NEW YEAR'S

Back in 1968, my friend Len Naismith from Australia told me about their Christmas and holiday times, and I wrote the column "Christmas Down Under." Last year, my friend from Switzerland, Conrad Schachenmann, related their holiday doings and the column was called "A Swiss Christmas." This year, when my Japanese friend, Harukazu Miki, was visiting us, I asked him to write me about Christmas and New Year's in Japan and the letter arrived just the other day.

He said that Christmas in Japan is not a national holiday because most of them are not Christians, so they don't have any religious reasons to celebrate Christmas. "Generally, it is the busiest day of the year for business, even for family life." They do know what our Christmas means, however, and more and more, the children are receiving gifts from Santa Claus. The presents are put in front of their pillows after they are asleep.

I did a little checking into Japanese religions. The two main ones are Buddhism and Shintoism. Buddhists practice the teachings of Gautama Buddha, believing that suffering is an inescapable part of life and that self-purification is the best path to follow. There are 12 different sects of Buddhism in Japan with 106,634 temples. Shintoism is based upon reverence of the spirits of natural forces, emperors, and heroes. It has 13 sects in Japan and more than 100,000 shrines. There are, however, several thousand Christian churches in Japan.

Emperor Hirohito is the 124th emperor of his line and was seventy-one years old in 1972. He renounced his emperor's divinity May 3, 1947, when the new Japanese constitution was ratified. That was also when Japan gave up its right to wage any further war. Not a bad idea for all of us.

So much for Christmas and religious doings. As Harukazu writes, "For the Japanese people, the New Year's days are the most important holidays." To capture the flavor of his letter, the following is verbatim. May I say that I'd hate to have to write to him in Japanese and capture the meanings, the spellings, the sentence structures and the like of his language and customs.

"Most of the offices and schools get into the holidays from December 28 until January 5. January 1, 2 and 3 are the national holidays. At the midnight of December 31, all of the shrine's bells in Japan starts hit of 108 times chime (they say we human beings have 108 bad ideas) to forget the bad things happened last year and pray for the better and great new year.

"Hearing the shrine's bell, family members say, 'Congratulations for the happy New Year' each other and they eat Japanese noodles which means good luck, then they go to bed.

"The morning of the New Year's Day is the most quiet time of the year. Each family celebrate with Toso, which is sweet Japanese sake (wine). They also have special New Year's food including rice cakes. They wear kimono in these days, especially women do. In front of everybody's home gate, they have the special decoration so called Matsukazari made by pine tree, bamboo and palm tree.

"Children have also special play for this season like kite, badminton, cards and spin a top.

"Only in these days, people greeting each other wherever they meet, on if road, train, theater, etc. even if they do not know each other."

Harukazu concluded his letter with the apology, "It is a

Harukazu Miki and R.G.G. belting out "On a Slow Boat to China"

very rough report so I am afraid that it would be able to
help you even a bit."

As the No. 1 son of a successful Japanese manufacturing
family, Harukazu Miki has been and is a delight to know
and is most entertaining and interesting. Barely more than
thirty years old, he represents the new breed of Japanese
encompassing a modern and swinging philosophy. He married a Japan Air Line stewardess, has traveled the world,
was educated partially in the United States, and now has
his own No. 1 son. My company has done business with his

family's company for many years and we regard them as the most efficient, honest, prompt, reliable and fun-to-do-business-with of any of our national and international accounts.

The picture shows Harukazu and me belting out a chorus of "On a Slow Boat to China" while circling Manhattan on a chartered boat during a company anniversary party. This well represents the relationship we have with him and his associates. It may be timely to point out that they are our customers and we sell them fifty times the dollar amount of goods that we buy back from them. If our national balance of trade with Japan were like that, we'd be in great shape.

Just before Harukazu's letter arrived the other day, we received from them the largest order ever sent us.

It was dated December 7.

December, 1972

"...the makeup of the gases in the air leads directly to smells...if smells could be documented, so could the pollution sources."

THE NOSE KNOWS

I have a very acute sense of smell and therefore, for me, a whole host of memories, classifications, and events are associated with odors.

The mere whiff of pungent smoke from the pinon pine being burned at Vail and Aspen brings visions of white slopes and friendly groups of skiers. A smell that I can't classify occurs every two or three years and immediately I'm once again pinned under the wreckage of the Lake Harriet pavilion as the roar of the 1925 tornado recedes into the distance.

At the end of a long evening of partying, I can barely remove my shirt for the smell of old cigarette and cigar smoke that has permeated it, yet chances are the stale odors are the only unpleasant remnants of the evening.

Smells are a form of pollution and if smells could ever be classified, a long step towards control of air pollution would be accomplished. It is terrible to see a long trail of dark vapors streaming from a jet plane, or to observe a tall chimney spewing black smoke into the air while some engineer is not doing his job, or to watch the change from year to year in the pall of pollution that clings to the eastern side of the Rockies around Denver, yellowish and so dissimilar to the clear mountain air of the past.

Determining the cause of air pollution is difficult, but the makeup of the gases in the air leads directly to smells and therefore if smells could be documented, so could the pollution sources. The causes of odors are almost unlimited, but there are four general types: fragrant, acidic, rancid, and burnt.

Smells are caused by molecules of chemicals that are free to enter our noses, which are then dissolved in the liquid of the olfactory organs in the top of our noses, stimulate the olfactory nerves that lead to the olfactory lobes in our brains, and are read by our brains as the odor of roses, onions, or some new thing that must be traced back and associated with an object or an experience.

In general, molecules — of which all things are made — are more active the warmer they get. Perfume on a person smells stronger than perfume in a bottle because the person's skin temperature causes the perfume molecules to be more active and therefore leave as a gas in greater numbers to attack the nose. Oftentimes a combination of molecules can give different smells under different sets of circumstances. A case in point is oak wood, which smells somewhat acidic when wet but smells entirely different when being burned.

Lately, I've become fascinated with the possibility of telling the history of a region and reading what is going to happen merely by smelling smoke. Sounds far-fetched, doesn't it? Maybe it is, but take our Minnetonka area as an example. Certain trees give off certain smells when burned, such as the marvelous nighttime odor of an oak fireplace fire, or hard sugar maple or white birch.

These smells result from the chemical molecules being given off. These chemicals are in the trees in those combinations because of the soils in which they grow. The soils are such because of the geologic history of the region.

Because of this history, our lakes can be classed as to certain kinds which have their own types of fish and weeds, pollution problems, and types of trees. If I was certain that wood from a specific area was being burned, I could tell you immediately whether or not the water offshore was good walleye fishing or not, what kinds of weeds occur in

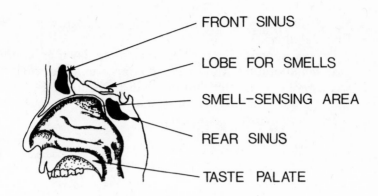

FRONT SINUS

LOBE FOR SMELLS

SMELL-SENSING AREA

REAR SINUS

TASTE PALATE

CROSS SECTION OF
THE HUMAN NOSE

the water, what kinds of minnows and other small fish play around in the shallows, what kinds of wildflowers grow along the shore — and so on until the whole spectrum of biological life was documented — merely from the smell of wood smoke.

I admit I'm over-simplifying the example, but the fact remains that smells are an important reliable key as to what is happening and what may happen. Smoke and smells chemically pollute our environment just as much as sewage and fertilizers chemically pollute our waters. We don't have unlimited water and we don't have unlimited air, so something's going to have to give.

What man is adding each year to the biosphere as part of smelly air pollution is staggering. In the United States, we are pumping into the air more than 164 million metric tons (663 billion 500 million pounds) of pollutants, one-half of which come from the automobile — mostly in the forms of carbon monoxide and hydrocarbons. Oxidants such as ozone and peroxycetyl nitrate from other sources cause a

45

$2,000,000 per year damage to ornamental growth in New England alone.

Do you suppose it's possible that some day a great-great-grandchild of mine won't have the opportunity to smell fine woodsmoke — that all burning will be banned? Perish the thought, but then maybe all mankind will have perished by that time, anyway.

January, 1970

"I wasn't prepared...for the reddish water and jello-pink slush...as the auger broke through the ice."

SURPRISE PACKAGES

Now that Christmas is over for another year and unless you have a birthday coming up soon, the package-opening routine will have to wait awhile for most of us. I admit that I just love to open packages, which is why I'm a nut about mail order and year around there's generally something on the way to me from someplace.

Possibly it's this curiosity as to what's inside the package that makes each Sunday morning a very special event. This is when I take my water samples and, especially during the winter with the ice and snow hiding the water, the anticipation of what will be found builds up all week.

I'm the first one to admit that a lot of the time it's downright uncomfortable out on the ice with winds dropping the wind-chill far below zero (my record while taking samples is 63 below), but when the sun is out, the wind is light, and the temperature is in the high 20s, nothing could be more pleasant. Over the years I've developed quite a routine and for the past year I have pulled a mobile lab behind my snowmobile. The lab is complete with all the motley gear that is collected when any kind of project is continually underway.

Although I have an ice chisel and a hand Finbore auger, my power Eskimo auger cuts through the ice in nothing flat, giving me a hole with a diameter large enough to work my algae seine up and down and to snake the sampling tube in and out with all of its various hoses, fittings, chains, and wires. Also, the resultant clean hole clearly shows the type of ice and it's very easy to measure the layers of snow, slush, loose and tight ice.

If you haven't punched a hole through the ice at one time or another, you should. It's a show by itself. The chips and shavings glint in the sun as they pour from the hole while being screwed out by the auger and when the light catches them just right, a play of color dances in and around the pile of sparkling chips. When the hole finally punctures through the bottom of the ice, a gush of water tumbles out from the weight of the snow on the ice and the release of pressure caused by the new hole. Being a petroleum geologist by training, I often romanticize that maybe I'm drilling for oil and that gush of water is black gold newly discovered.

I wasn't prepared, however, one Sunday early in January, 1969, for the reddish water and jello-pink slush and ice shavings that materialized as the auger broke through the ice. The sight was shocking, the smell was awful, and my plankton net dripped pink as if blood had been seined. Rushing into the house, I announced to my wife that I wished every soul in the country could be standing on the ice to see this terrible sight — then there would be no trouble bringing the Freshwater Biological Institute into existence.

Oscillatoria rubescens is the name of the alga causing this pink stain. It has been in our waters before, just like it has been in almost all other fresh waters. It has, possibly, bloomed as severely in times past as that day in our Minnetonka. It has been the dominant alga in Minnetonka for the past five or six weeks, and I observed it floating as pink puffs of cotton underneath the transparent ice for the first two or three days after the freeze in December. But never have I seen it in such a severe bloom; it can't help but shake you up.

However, the bloom is not what really does the shaking. It's the almost total lack of knowledge about the Oscillatoria family that is the shocker. Some say that although it is not

Equipment used for taking water samples through the ice

a positive indicator, it loves polluted waters. Some say severe blooms have been noticed in years past in Michigan lakes after the ice went out. Textbooks list many members of the Oscillatoria family and have it placed in the division Cyanophyta, class of Myxophyceae, and order Oscillatoriales. But beyond the average documentation of length, cell structure, colors, reproduction habits and such, knowledge is extremely slim about the effects of light, heat, water temperatures, chemicals, and currents on its growth and living habits.

The Oscillatoria family is called that because although they are plants, they can move with a spiral or oscillatory motion of the body, a back-and-forth motion of some of the cells or a waving of the end of its strand. The redness of these algae is caused by a pigment called c-phycoerythrin in the chromoplasm.

Now do you see why it's fascinating to open up the lake each Sunday morning? Talk about surprise packages!! People ask me what the lake is going to be like next week or next month or next summer and I reply with a guess tempered by the statement that nobody can really tell and anything can happen because we don't know very much at all. We're going to learn — we have to learn — but we better get on the stick because time is running out. It's great to have our lake water nice and clear right now, but we don't know why it is, how long it will stay so, or what will happen next except we do know algae, weed, and animal blooms will continue to come and go. Our goal is to understand and control them.

January, 1970

"Two of us didn't bother to tell Mr. Dick that
we were moving in with him — we just did."

THE TALE OF A MOUSE

My name is Minnie and I don't particularly like it. Ever
since Mr. Disney named Mickey Mouse's wife Minnie, all
female mice have been called that, and judging from the
number of lady mice in the world, you can imagine it
doesn't give me much individuality.

I have been living in Mr. Dick's house since the cold
Minnesota weather arrived around the early part of December. As far as I know, I was born about a year ago and
grew up in and out of Mr. Dick's outside garage, along with
my two sisters and two brothers.

I assume I look pretty much as they do, being an absolutely gorgeous white-footed mouse (please excuse the
vanity, but I am pretty). My eyes may be large and bulge
a little, but they help me see in the dark. My ears are big,
and kind of floppy, but they help me hear all sorts of things.
Apparently, I'm a *Peromyscus leocopus* (I think that's what
Mr. Dick said one evening), and now that I'm a full-grown
female, I'm about four inches long with a three-inch tail
lightly covered with hairs. I try to keep my white belly nice
and white so it contrasts beautifully with the fawn brown
of my sides and back. That slightly darker stripe down my
back looks rather sporty, if you ask me.

How we loved Mr. Dick's garage! It was simply loaded
with goodies like sunflower and saffron seeds and whole

kernel corn — and those delightful gunny sacks were so cozy to snuggle into when those nights turned cool in the fall. But, oh my! How cold it became in December, and my father had told us to head for a warm house to spend the long winters.

Two of us didn't bother to tell Mr. Dick that we were moving in with him — we just did. Imagine our surprise to discover plenty of fine food and water in his greenhouse and excellent company in his diamond dove, who became our good friend.

My brother and I loved to chase around the greenhouse shelves. The only drawback was that we liked to sleep during the day and play at night. That dove is quiet as a mouse all night long and then coos and flutters and stomps around to disturb us during the day. We decided the dove was worth the trouble, however, because of the excellent food and lodging provided.

It wasn't long before we discovered the warm air register in the greenhouse wall where my brother and I would curl up and sleep away the days. In the evening, we'd take over the greenhouse, and many was the time I'd sit on a shelf by an inside window and watch Mr. Dick in his house. Once in a while, he'd come over and talk to me and I'd get all nervous and lick my feet, wiggle my ears (which made him laugh), and then vibrate my front feet to make a drumming sound.

One morning my brother was missing, and two days later I watched as Mr. Dick lifted the small, quiet body from the bottom of a shaft that was called a dumb waiter. I was afraid of that place because of its high sides and no food or water.

A few days later, Mr. Dick placed a metal thing in the greenhouse with two nice pieces of cheese on it and I could hardly wait until it was dark to investigate. When the time came, I crawled in, there was a noise, and I couldn't get out. I was frantic and ran around for hours until Mr. Dick came back, lifted me up in the metal thing and carried me to another room where he put me in a larger metal thing. As soon as he left, I found an opening by a bent wire and crawled out, finding myself in his basement.

White-Footed Mouse

I had the run of the place and really enjoyed myself. I found some more saffron seed and there was water in the furnace room. Funny thing, but after a few days I felt kind of heavy and could see that I was certainly putting on weight. A strange urge came over me and I found an old dresser drawer with a colorful scarf in it and I carried lots of seeds to the drawer after I had rearranged the scarf into a nice soft pile.

And then I noticed that smaller metal thing again with more yummy cheese in it. I didn't want to do it but I just couldn't resist that cheese — and there I was, caught again. I was so excited I ran back and forth, and then I started to give birth to my babies. Mr. Dick was there and he was excited, too. As fast as he could, he transferred me and two babies (by this time) to the larger cage, tore up some rags for me, and by the end of the afternoon, I had five little ones to care for. I gathered the rags into a pile, nudged and pushed my babies into a smaller pile on the rags, and fell into a deep sleep.

The next morning, Mr. Dick took four of the babies away. I was worried about them because they seemed so still and cold, but the one that was left was brightly pink and squirming like mad.

The morning after that, Mr. Dick took the fifth one away for probably the same reason — it was so still and cold — and I was so lonesome and still am. The larger cage (with the bent wire fixed so I can't get out) is nice but I don't like it. There's food and water but no freedom. There's a track that goes around and around when I run on it, but I can't go anywhere. This is not my kind of life.

I wonder who's better off — my brother or me?

The tale of the mouse is true. As soon as I finish typing these words, Minnie will no longer be in the larger cage and she will have freedom again. I won't tell you — or my wife — what that freedom is.

January, 1972

"...raindrops falling through clean air have contained more organic matter than an equal volume of lake water...."

CLEAN AIR IS ONLY RELATIVE

How clean is clean? Now there's a question that comes to the very heart of so many of our environmental problems. We want nice clean water, nice clean air, nice clean this and that — but when you come right down to it, what we're talking about is a controlled amount of dirtiness.

Absolutely pure water won't support life. Absolutely pure air would signal the end to rainfall and the source of essential vitamins and minerals. Our problems today relate to man's unsettling of the natural balance of impurities that occurs in our environment and the terrible consequences resulting from this imbalance.

Did you know that in our atmosphere — our air — important vitamins are manufactured? It's true — such vitamins as B-12 and biotin and niacin. Did you know that many times it has been found that raindrops falling through relatively clean air have contained more organic matter than an equal volume of lake water? And did you know that it's becoming more and more positive that great life goes on in the clouds and upper reaches of our atmosphere?

It has been proved many times that huge varieties and quantities of matter are in the air. Besides our important gases of carbon dioxide, oxygen, and nitrogen, there are other natural substances such as nitrous oxide, ammonium, sulfur dioxide, carbon monoxide, methane, butane, acetone, and butyl alcohol. Other things not naturally made in the atmosphere are carried aloft by up-drafts; thus, one finds phosphorous, potassium, calcium, magnesium, and iron in the clouds. Add to these things such aeroplankton as bacteria, fungi, algae — and pollen and feathers and spiders and seeds and insects, all having been found way up there — and we now can agree there is no such thing as absolutely pure air in our atmosphere.

The air is only a part of our entire system and what air does or doesn't do has its own effect on everything else. Our usual atmosphere is made up of about 21 percent oxygen (25 times the concentration in lake water) and 78 percent nitrogen. That makes 99 percent and the remaining 1 percent is composed of other gases and chemicals, the most common being carbon dioxide (.03 percent).

During the past aeons of time, life as we know it on earth has struck a fine balance based upon the amount of light and heat and such that have been available to the earth from outer sources. What we as "intelligent" men are doing

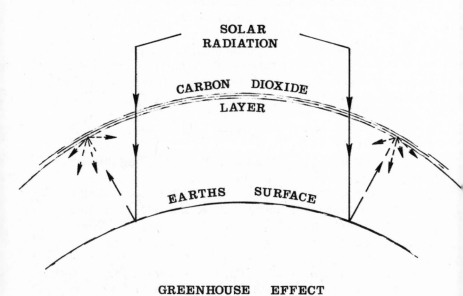

SOLAR RADIATION

CARBON DIOXIDE LAYER

EARTHS SURFACE

GREENHOUSE EFFECT
(TO WARM UP THE EARTH)

is upsetting the natural state of the air and altering the patterns of our lives. It's not enough that we are pumping strange things into the air — DDT and mercaptans of sulfur, for instance — but also serious quantities of dirt and critical chemicals that can easily tip our life balances as we know them today.

There are two main theories as to how we are altering our weather and therefore our ways of life in the immediate future by unnaturally contaminating our atmosphere. One theory — the greenhouse theory — states that excessive carbon dioxide, essentially from automobiles, is building up in our air, forming a layer of gas as in a greenhouse which keeps great amounts of solar energy from bouncing off the earth and back into the atmosphere. The result will be a warming up of the earth, a melting of the polar ice caps and a rise in the sea levels of over 200 feet — flooding New York and Los Angeles and countless other cities.

The other theory by Bryson states that excessive dust in the atmosphere keeps an increasing amount of solar energy

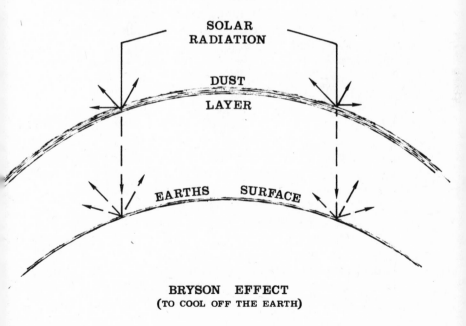

SOLAR RADIATION

DUST LAYER

EARTHS SURFACE

BRYSON EFFECT
(TO COOL OFF THE EARTH)

from reaching the earth, resulting in a cooling of the surface and a return of an ice age — all to occur so rapidly that he looks for a new ice age to start within thirty years. Bryson further states that this dust is beyond our American control because the great majority of it is coming from China, India, and Africa as a result of poor but aggressive agricultural practices.

Obviously, our problems are worldwide. Just the other day, an Italian town named itself "stinkville" (I didn't get the Italian name) because of its air and water pollution. Tokyo, Japan allows policemen "breath breaks" every two hours or so because of car exhaust pollution in the streets.

The air affects the water, the water affects the soil, the soil and water affect the air — and round and round and round. We're all part of a great and complex system with checks and balances that shouldn't be upset. As a parting thought, realize that raindrops form around impurities — dust particles and such, but usually around bits of nitrites, which become a major source of nitrogen for us. But raindrops are really very diluted lake water and contain other things like sodium, potassium, calcium, magnesium, chlorine, barium, iodine, iron, hydrogen, oxygen, phosphorous, carbon, silicon, and aluminum. Without these trace minerals and such, our life wouldn't be what we have had and now have. Some of these impurities in our air are essential.

The big question is how much.

You may sometimes wonder where certain minerals and vitamins originate when found in our waters and the air. Here's one such source — a feed called Triple Action Horse and Pony feed by the manufacturer. It contains the following: "Crimped oats, cracked corn, rolled barley, dehulled soybean meal, linseed meal, dehydrated alfalfa meal, condensed fermented corn extractives, cane molasses, wheat middlings, dried whey-products, condensed fish solubles, corn germ meal, corn bran, yeast culture, animal fat (preserved with BHA, citric acid), calcium carbonate, dicalcium phosphate, salt, D-Activated plant Sterol (source of vitamin D-2), Vitamin A Palmitate (stability improved), d-Alpha Tocopheryl Acetate (source of vitamin E activity), niacin, riboflavin supplement, vitamin B-12 supplement, choline chloride, folic acid, calcium pantothenate, thiamine hydrochloride, pyridoxine hydrochloride, maganese sulfate, zinc oxide, red iron oxide, iron sulfate, magnesium oxide, copper oxide, cobalt carbonate, ethylene diamine dihydriodide, natural and artifical flavor added and ethoxyquin (a preservative)."

February, 1971

"Bedtime was easy. He seldom wears shoes anyway, so the socks sort of fell off."

BRADLEY SPENDS THE NIGHT

"How come there's water under the ice, Grandpa?"

That question — and a thousand others — were posed by Bradley during his first overnight stay with us. We picked him up before supper Saturday night and he returned home Sunday noon. In between, the mind and personality of a fascinating young boy filled the house.

It appeared that the visit was starting on a bad note when Bradley left his house, jumped in our car, and suddenly became very quiet and was close to weeping all the way to our house. He finally explained he saw Grandma's needle-point work in our car and realized he had left his behind. He cheered up when I explained I didn't have any needle-point to do, either.

He was soon settled in the den in front of the fireplace with a roaring fire — coloring table in full view of the TV, crayon box neatly to one side and an outline of a candle to color, to match one of the seven candles flickering near him. He had helped me lay the fire, crumpling the newspapers while remarking "that's cooperation" — a new word for him learned from TV's Electric Company.

The Gopher-Iowa basketball game started and he said, "Oh, boy! Basketball is my favorite game!" And then, "Which color am I for, Grandpa?"

I told him gold.

Bradley investigates a pair of binoculars

At half-time we played Go to the Dump, and it's impossible for small hands to handle a bunch of big cards. Upside down, backwards, one at a time, three at a time — all was part of the game. Somehow or another, it seemed to work out all right.

Band music on TV makes our diamond dove "coo" and Bradley was sure the bird was trying to tell him something during the game. He asked me what, and I satisfied him by stating that the bird was not booing but instead was cheering for the Gophers by telling them to "shoot — shoot." But being a bird, it had trouble with SHs and Ts and it came out "Coo — Coo."

It was a most pleasant Saturday evening at home.

Bedtime was easy. He seldom wears shoes anyway, so

the socks sort of fell off. His pajamas didn't look like pajamas with big numerals on the chest and blue pants looking for all the world like sweat pants. Visions of snowmobile rides and greenhouse watering in the morning put him to sleep for the night — after he "oh'd" and "ah'd" at the full moon and the light snow on the lake and the three-foot drift of snow atop the picnic table on the front deck.

We ate breakfast together, he with his fruit-pops and applesauce, I with my juice and bacon and eggs — and he was really excited to see the beautiful sunrise over Wawatosa Island near where his Mom and Dad spend summer nights anchored to shore with their houseboat. Even though it was 16 below, he was ready for the outdoors and only typing in my office and spraying water in the greenhouse, with a fast game of Concentration sandwiched in between, held him in until the morning air warmed to 2 below and out we went.

Bradley had never seen a hole drilled in the ice and his eyes were wide as the power auger bucked and bit ever deeper, until through it went! — and water gushed out of the hole and covered the surrounding snow. We carefully compared depths at which the secchi disk could still be seen (he a little deeper because he was closer to the ice) and all the little "bugs" darting about in the concentrated water sample brought a dead-serious look on his face as he silently pondered them. He pushed some snow back into the water in the ice hole and found out that snow floats in water. Neither of us noticed the cold.

His Dad picked him up in time to make a neighborhood hockey game, but not before we again played the record of Southern Swamp Noises torn out from the *Audubon Magazine* and he retrieved an empty small applejuice can and stuffed it into his suitcase. He said good-bye and thank-you to us and to the bird and to Molly, the dog, laying a tiny hand on Molly's head as he walked out the door.

Suddenly, the house was very quiet.

By the way, Bradley is barely 4 ½.

February, 1972

"Every little sound was bounced around.
Squirrels scratched and scraped climbing
the trees...."

ICE STORMS

Not only was the ice storm of last weekend a beautiful one,
but I can't remember when the after-conditions were such
that the ice remained for two or three days — a real fairy-
land. Because the ice did stay around, I had a chance to
make several observations about things that aren't normally
possible after this type of storm.

The most noticeable thing was the noise. After a snowfall,
the silence is almost deafening, a quietness that is eerie and
thick and unnatural as the snow blanket absorbs the sound
waves. Not so after an ice storm. Every little sound was
bounced around. Squirrels scratched and scraped climbing
the trees, cars roared, and snowmobiles were especially
noisy without under-snow to deaden the sound and only
ice to compound the sound.

I was up early Monday morning to let the dog out, and
it was still dark when I called her in. She wasn't in sight,
but as soon as I called, I could hear her coming. Each step
was a tinkling crunch as she broke through the snow crust.
An occasional thin slab would go sliding along the top of
the ice cover and make a raspy sound. Her invisible approach was very similar to the experience of three years
ago when, in Canada, I sat on a shoreline listening to a huge
moose slosh through the shallows in water up to his belly,
grunting and complaining, making a combination of weird

sounds I heard without being able to see the source. I finally did see him, by the way, and I figured he was undoubtedly on his way to find more moose moss to munch.

The cohesiveness of the ice from the storm was amazing. In some cases, as the ice loosened in the sun, the whole form of the ice on yard lights, mailboxes, and street signs slid off intact instead of in little pieces or drip by drip.

I felt for the birds and animals. They seemed to have survived the storm but food and water were problems. Hairy and downy woodpeckers were numerous at our feeder, and I don't think it was just a coincidence that two dead raccoons were on Highway 7 Monday morning after none had been seen all winter.

How do ice storms happen? There have been times when the outside temperature was in the teens, yet it rained. Why didn't the rain freeze before reaching the ground? Well, there is a logical explanation for all of this.

Water is strange anyway, but especially when it gets cool. It is heaviest at 39.2 degrees F. and grows lighter as it approaches freezing at 32 degrees F. because of a rearranging of its internal structure. Sometimes, however, water becomes "super-cool" and can be much colder than 32 degrees F. without freezing. High-flying aircraft have found water droplets still liquid at 58 degrees below zero, so it's feasible to have rain composed of drops already below the freezing point.

Now, a second thing happens. Water cools much faster when in contact with a solid object than in the air. So, down comes super-cooled rain and the instant it hits telephone lines, tree branches, or other cold solid objects, the extra cold transferred to the drops causes them to freeze right then and coat the object. Haven't you ever wondered why a thin round wire could be evenly coated all around with ice rather than have rain, as it falls, gradually freeze as it drops off? Instant freezing does it.

Cold rain and cold fog are pretty much the same — the main difference being in the size of drops. Fog can be regarded as a very low cloud. For rain to fall, tiny drops of moisture must join up with other drops until they are

The aftermath of an ice storm

65

heavy enough to fall. Most cloud droplets are only 2/2,500 of an inch in diameter and must grow to at least 1/125 of an inch before falling. Usually, a drop forms around an impurity in the air and starts as a tiny bit of ice around the impurity. Artificial "seeding" of a cloud to cause rain demonstrates this point: a sliver of dry ice the size of a grain of rice is enough to cause a rain shower from a large cumulus cloud.

Nothing is prettier than a rising sun shining on our wonderful world after an ice storm. These storms don't happen too often, thank goodness. But when they do, we might as well rise above them and drink in the sights. I wonder how St. Paul's super-mayor in his super-car got along in the super-cooled rain? Probably simply super.

February, 1971

"...under the microscope they make the
water sample look like Times Square...
on New Year's Eve."

WINTER WATER WONDERLAND

Sparkling water ruffled by a springtime breeze, wild white caps spurred on by a summer thunderstorm, dark cold waves matching the low scudding clouds of a windy fall day — water in motion is seemingly an indication of the activity that goes on below its surface.

In contrast, the frozen stillness of the lake in winter seems to infer that all is at rest, worn out from the warmer months and charging its batteries, so to speak, in preparation for the coming spring.

Such restfulness in winter is not the case by any means. True, the frogs, turtles, and similar forms have buried themselves in the muck while awaiting the warm-up of the water, and many forms of weeds have collapsed to the bottom of the lake to patiently pass the winter. But most fish are still active, certain types of weeds continue to photosynthesize and expel oxygen, and the water under the ice is really jumping with fascinating forms of algae (plants) and protozoa (animals). They are usually too small to see with the naked eye, but under the microscope they make the water sample look like Times Square in New York City on New Year's Eve.

Among the multitude of things present in the winter water is my favorite — animals barely visible to the naked eye as dancing and darting white specks in a concentrated water sample. They are called Daphnia and are fine fellows (well, my textbook says that most of them are partheno-genetic, which means the females produce eggs without fertilization by the males, and that certainly doesn't give either the male or female much fun!) that constantly pump water through their transparent bodies to get their food.

As the water passes through, the food is sifted and filtered, chewed and digested, and finally ejected as tiny green clumps. Their eyes are dark and exotic, constantly in motion, pushed and pulled by three strong muscles.

Daphnia come in many variations, but most of them are roly-poly with their chins tucked in and a serene look on their faces. Their reproduction output is better than man's, producing as many as twenty eggs at a time, but that's a piker compared to a walleye pike female that lays as many as 100,000 eggs.

Being transparent, they're fun to watch. Their hearts beat like mad and the eyes swing back and forth. They have no "lungs," so the vital exchange of gases like oxygen and nitrogen occurs through the surface of their legs and other parts of the body.

All Daphnia are classed as relatively simple and low forms of animal life.

A typical — and beautiful — alga in the water is a star-like diatom called asterionella — and they are lovely, fragile, and graceful with radiating spokes of soft amber hue, a jewel that is present in huge numbers in the cool waters during the spring before and after the ice goes out. A diatom is a special kind of algae that belongs to the division Chrysophyta because of their brownish color, and to the family Fragilariaceae.

All diatoms have a skeleton or body made up mostly of silicon compounds (common sand is silica) which gives them a yellowish-brown cast. Preferring cool water (under the ice, too), all diatoms in our lake are very numerous right now. If you look at the lake water early in the morning before the sun starts the green algae to working, the water has a distinctly brown cast because of the diatoms and may even taste fishy because of their numbers. Of the many

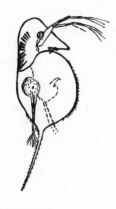
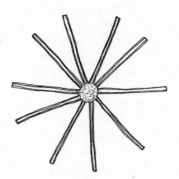

DAPHNIA (25x)   ASTERIONELLA   (250 x)

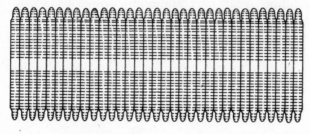

FRAGILLARIA   (500x)

diatoms, Asterionella leads the Minnetonka pack.

This water star has a central soft hub with spokes radiating out from the hub to terminate in somewhat clubby ends. Under the microscope, two or more Asterionella may over-lap and look like a latticework of slender arms. Along with these stars, other diatoms add great fascination to the water samples: round flying saucers called Stephanodiscus and Coscinodiscus; multi-toothed "combs" called Fragellaria with arms extending from both sides of a central rib; and crazy things called Tabellaria whose various joints hang haphazardly together as if you were trying to put a series of short lines end to end with your eyes closed.

Diatoms are very useful things. They occur in both fresh and salt water (depending upon the type), are found free

in the water or clinging to rocks and reeds, and are remark-
ably tough. Some have been found in dry soil after forty-
eight years and yet grew when moistened. One of the main
commercial uses for diatoms is in diatomaceous earth —
an excellent filtering material because of the "airy" yet
dense condition of countless billions of skeletons accumu-
lating on the ocean or lake floor upon death of the diatom.
Solid beds of diatom skeletons many feet thick are regularly
mined — with the largest all-time deposit having been discovered while drilling for oil in California, where conditions
at one time were so perfect that the diatom bed is nearly
3,000 feet thick.

The fascination of observing microscopic plants and
animals from the water — under the ice or no — is a
never-ending treat, a continuous wondrous show that's
hard to beat. There's a beauty in everything.

February, 1968
April, 1969

"Now I know why Twiggy was so named...
a small shoot undeveloped in more ways
than one!"

TWIGS AND BUDS

Sometime ago, while reading up on trees and shrubs, I learned that the easiest and surest way for species identification was to collect and examine the twigs and buds during the wintertime while growth was dormant but ready for spring.

This surprised me as I always have believed that leaves, flowers, bark and the like were the best ways to identify species and varieties. To satisfy my curiosity, I located a twig and bud book as well as an excellent chart printed by the Audubon Society — and I find that the statement is correct. Not only are no two budding characteristics the same, but there is a remarkable dissimilarity that makes it easy to tell one from another.

First of all, however, I wanted to be sure what is a twig and what is a bud. Per the dictionary, a twig is a small shoot or branch. It also means fashion or style in British usage. A bud is an undeveloped shoot or stem and also a person or thing not yet mature. Now I know why Twiggy was so named a couple of years ago — an English fashion model, and a small shoot undeveloped in more ways than one!

Buds turn into twigs that have flowers or leaves. A bud is usually covered with bud scales for protection and it's really amazing how these supposedly tender things can survive our weather — not only the severity but the fluctuations from warm suns to icy blasts. The scales in their many forms keep the buds from drying out and also protect them from physical damage. Some of these scales are very waxy, like the cottonwood, and some very hairy, like the pussy willow.

There are three general kinds of buds — leaf buds like the cottonwood, flower buds like the apples and lilacs, and mixed buds like the oak. Buds are further defined by their location — either terminal, at the tip of an old twig, or lateral, along the body of the twig. The lateral buds are classed as to their way of growth — opposite, with pairs opposite to each other on the stem; alternate, with a more or less spiral arrangement along the stem; or whorled, with three or more buds around the stem at pretty much the same height.

Two weeks ago, I trudged out in the cold and cut several branches from a variegated type of red-twig dogwood and some whips from pretty French pussy willows that I had planted in a low spot two years ago in the back of our property. Both varieties were dormant, of course, but it only took three days for the pussy willow buds to come to life while nearly two weeks passed before the dogwood showed some growth. I love pussy willow with their dark chocolate-brown bud scales parted by a silver-gray tongue of fuzz as the growth starts.

Sunday, I again sallied forth to collect some common twigs with their buds ready for late March or April. I purposely chose things which anybody can find and if you're so inclined, I suggest you take five minutes, collect a few, and see for yourself the differences and the beauty of nature's growth in the bud stage.

Sugar Maple — buds are a soft medium brown with very regular overlapping of the bud scales on the terminal bud and opposite lateral buds occurring at the very base of the terminal bud. It's easy to see why hard sugar maples grow so slowly.

Green Ash — pretty deep maroon terminal buds that look like they've been sprinkled with white sugar. The leaf scars

Chickadee on a Maple Twig

from last year look like the huge lower lips of the Ubangi tribe.

Cottonwood — buds are very waxy, tight and yellowish-brown. I clipped two different trees. One was smooth and slender with one terminal bud and three small lateral buds over a three-inch span (a male tree?) while the other had big fat buds including a large terminal and five lateral buds in less than three inches (the female?).

Apple — large rough buds with dark brown bud scales and delicate silver hairs.

Mountain Ash — old flower bracts at end of twig. Terminal bud at the base of the flower stem. Deep brown bud scales with silvery hairy bud body hanging out with tobacco-stained whiskers.

Lilac — beautifully healthy terminal buds and opposite laterals. Their color is reddish olive-brown like a roasted chestnut. I cut a fat terminal bud in cross-section and under my pocket glass a miniature lilac bloom lay nestled in the bud with breathtaking repose.

Silver Maple — small terminal bud with alternate laterals. Everything is covered with fine silver hairs and dust. Buds are a light taffy-brown.

Willow — a straight-growing variety. Terminal buds and alternate laterals are long, slender, smooth, and a medium yellow with bases silvery and everything as if sprinkled with salt.

It's so frustrating to know so little and have limited time to learn and observe. I would love to look at everything and collect it and understand it and appreciate it. The alternative, I guess, is to use what time is available and make the most of it. It certainly is satisfying and the marvels of nature are unending.

February, 1970

"The main trouble with selling by catalog today is the increased mobility of the buying public."

SEED CATALOG TIME

New car fever is a tough disease for a man to fight. New dress fever causes the temperatures of both the wife and husband to rise — if for different reasons. But for the gardening breed — young or old, married or single, male or female — the mid-winter arrivals of the numerous seed and garden catalogs are nearly impossible to resist, let alone ignore.

For more years than I care to admit, well before the Victory Gardens of World War II, for instance, I have been an avid coupon sender-inner, catalog receiver, page peruser, luscious-growth believer — and occasionally a purchaser with dreams of good things to come as I slip the completed form with money into the mailbox.

While rearranging the basement last weekend, I came across my detailed planting record for the year 1942. It certainly pointed up the change in costs, but even with the drastic cost increases in seed and plants that has occurred, today's selling by free catalogs has to be phasing out.

Thirty years ago, the average vegetable seed packet cost five cents; today, the cost is between 25 cents and 50 cents. Mary Washington asparagus was the staple then and still is, and I bought 50 plants from the Whitten Nursery in Bridgman, Michigan, for 90 cents; an average price today is 25 plants for $4.95. Just compare the following, 30 years apart:

	1942	1972
Red MacDonald Rhubarb	6 for $1.20	2 for $2.75
Rancocas Blueberry	3 for 1.70	3 for 6.25
Everbearing Strawberry	25 for .75	25 for 4.95
Red Raspberry	39 for 1.89	30 for 19.00
6-8 foot apple, plum and pear trees	$1 each	$5 to $8 each

My best buys in 1942 happened when two neighbors gave me things: Atherton Bean contributed 50 Norway pine, 50 Colorado spruce, 100 American elm and 100 soft maple seedlings; and Mary Corrigan gave me five packets of seed — presumably to plant for her. The seeds that I bought came from the Interstate Nursery, Hamburg, Iowa; Danish Seed Co., Minneapolis; or were Northrup King seeds from Nagell's Hardware (remember?).

Selling seeds and plants by mail is still big business, although now and for the past many years, I, at least, have bought all but very special ones at our local places of business. To get some of the better seed catalogs today, you usually have to buy the book and then get a rebate on your first real order.

In my opinion, the finest garden catalog (costs $5) is from Wayside Gardens, Mentor, Ohio. The current issue is 208 pages, all in true color, and amongst the many things listed is a special interest index which categorizes what to plant for special effects, such as an all-white garden or a wildflower garden or a garden for moist areas.

A suggested Winter Interest Garden should include *Corylus contora* with its twisted branches, giving it the popular name of Harry Lauder's Walking Stick; or Cornus Coral Beauty, a special coral-red dogwood whose colorful branches give a fine effect against the white of the snow.

A Hummingbird Garden should have:

Lobelia cardinals or Cardinal flower
Asclepias tuberosa or Butterfly weed
Aquilegia spring song, a special new giant columbine
Monarda adam or Bee balm
Oenothera tetragona or Evening primrose
Penstemon firebird or Beard tongue.

The suggested Audubon Collection seems interesting; not only does it provide food for the birds, but the berries are so colorful:

Aronia arbutifolia or Chokeberry — white flowers and red berries

Comus kousa chinensis or Milky Way dogwood — its fruit is strawberry-like

Cotoneaster Sealing Wax — shiny green leaves and red berries

Ligustrum obtusesfolium regelianum or Regal's privet — with blue-black berries

Pyracanta lalandi or Firethorn — an evergreen with white flowers and orange-scarlet berries

Viburnum opulus xanthocarpum or Golden-fruited cranberry — its berries are a golden yellow.

Recently, I talked with an executive of Farmer's Seed and Nursery Co. in Faribault to find out some of the inside workings of the seed catalog business. This happens to be Farmer's eightieth year and they are sending out 700,000 catalogs of various shapes and sizes during three general periods. In the past, the average order received by mail totalled between $8 and $9. Of the thousands of items in the catalog, strawberry plants rank number one in dollar volume, followed by gladiola bulbs and then potatoes.

The main trouble with selling by catalog today is the increased mobility of the buying public. It's nothing to get into the family car and drive many miles to buy what once was ordered by mail. The reason for a catalog today is to present detailed information with a wide range of selection so a person has been pre-sold before the actual time of purchase.

One thing I remember year after year in the Farmer's catalog is not a beautiful seed or plant picture but an advertisement for gopher traps with a rangy Grant Wood type of gentleman standing by a string of gophers. This man has helped sell traps by mail since 1936. His name is an improbable one — Bluejay Durham, a Faribault, Minnesota farmer. Bluejay saw his picture in only a couple of catalog issues, however. His Model T Ford went through the ice of Cedar Lake near Faribault in the late '30s and he drowned.

As each year passes, the costs of preparing, printing, and distributing catalogs increase and I suppose fewer and fewer will be available. What a pity! The arrival of the catalogs and the dreams of planting glory ease the trials of snow drifts and icy roads. We need *something* to get us through to springtime!

February, 1968
February, 1972

Bluejay Durham

"...man...has been constantly bugged
by the fact that a lunar month isn't made
up of an even number of 24-hour days...."

LEAP YEAR

Who will celebrate his fifth official birthday Tuesday but yet can vote, buy a drink in New York City, and is eligible for the draft? Right — a Leap Year male born February 29, 1952.

Leave it to the French to start the custom of having the ladies invite the men on "Leap Day," but that extra day every four years in February has a couple of other advantages. Leap Year is an American presidential year and candidates have an extra day to talk and talk, and we welcome the extra day at our office as it gives us one more business day in an otherwise too-short month.

About every nine seconds, a baby is born in the United States, which adds up to 3,500,000 per year (even at our present lower birth rate). This means that on Tuesday, February 29, 1972, about 10,000 babies will pucker up their faces to the light of day and will join the other living members of the select February 29 group who number around 172,500 within our total population of well over 210 million in America.

Why do we have Leap Years? Because we're sun and moon oriented, that's why. When you think about it, our lives are run by three cycles that deal with time: night and day (24 hours), a year (365 days), and the lunar month (about 29 ½ days). Since before Christ, man has devised calendars based upon the lunar month but has been constantly bugged by the fact that a lunar month isn't made up of an even number of 24-hour days — so he has tried to devise several different ways to make up the difference every once in a while. In our calendar, Leap Year is the result.

The real problem of calendars as we know them is two-fold: A year is not 365 days long but rather 365 days 5 hours 48 minutes and 46 seconds long. Also, the lunar month of 29 ½ days just doesn't jibe with having even days, so we have 28, 30, or 31 days in a month. The forerunner of our present calendar (*kalends* in Latin) was put together by the pontifex maximus Julius Caesar, and the so-called Julian calendar was used from 46 B.C. to A.D. 1582.

The extra hours and days in all of those years, however, were really messing things up — so Pope Gregory XIII took the work done by the Venerable Bede, a Benedictine monk who had figured out the extra hours in a year, and did three things to make our present-day so-called Gregorian calendar: He added 11 days to October 4 of A.D. 1583, making it October 15; he declared every fourth year, or a year divisible by four, to be a Leap Year with an extra day added; and he declared that each century-year divisible by four will *not* have an extra day added, meaning that the years 1600, 2000, 2400 and such would not be Leap Years.

I asked myself why the Pope added 11 days, so I worked the following out: From 46 B.C. to A.D. 1582, a total of 1,628 years had elapsed. We now know that an extra day is needed about every four years to keep the seasons and such straight. By not doing that during the 1,628 years, 407 extra days had accumulated. Deduct one whole year of 365 days from the 407 days and you have 42 days left to adjust. The Pope was working with the month of October with 31 days, so by deducting that amount from 42 days, he arrived with 11 days left. He took the 11 days, added them to October 4 and came up with October 15 and all corrections were made — just like that. Pretty smart, these Popes.

Britain and its American colonies didn't switch to the

Gregorian calendar until 1752 and dates prior to that year are marked by the prefix O.S. for "old style." Old books carry George Washington's birthday as February 11, 1732 (OS), instead of February 22, 1732, per the Gregorian calendar. France switched in 1806, Japan in 1873, China in 1912, Greece in 1924, and Turkey in 1927.

There are still countries that don't follow the Gregorian calendar at all and there are some countries like China that adopted the Gregorian calendar but still retain their own type of calendar at the same time. The Chinese lunar calendar has 12 months alternating between 29 and 30 days per month and each 30 months they throw in an extra month. They also name their years after 12 animals. 1972 is the Year of the Rat, and 1973 will be the Year of the Ox. Dragons, roosters, and tigers are some of the other animals.

The Hebrew calendar is similar to the old Chinese lunar calendar. Each month starts just after the new moon and months alternate between 29 and 30 days long. Every two or three years, an extra month is added.

14   1972

JANUARY								MAY								SEPTEMBER						
S	M	T	W	T	F	S	S	M	T	W	T	F	S	S	M	T	W	T	F	S
						1		1	2	3	4	5	6						1	2
2	3	4	5	6	7	8	7	8	9	10	11	12	13	3	4	5	6	7	8	9
9	10	11	12	13	14	15	14	15	16	17	18	19	20	10	11	12	13	14	15	16
16	17	18	19	20	21	22	21	22	23	24	25	26	27	17	18	19	20	21	22	23
23	24	25	26	27	28	29	28	29	30	31				24	25	26	27	28	29	30
30	31																			

FEBRUARY								JUNE								OCTOBER						
S	M	T	W	T	F	S	S	M	T	W	T	F	S	S	M	T	W	T	F	S
		1	2	3	4	5				1	2	3	1	2	3	4	5	6	7
6	7	8	9	10	11	12	4	5	6	7	8	9	10	8	9	10	11	12	13	14
13	14	15	16	17	18	19	11	12	13	14	15	16	17	15	16	17	18	19	20	21
20	21	22	23	24	25	26	18	19	20	21	22	23	24	22	23	24	25	26	27	28
27	28	29					25	26	27	28	29	30		29	30	31				

MARCH								JULY								NOVEMBER						
S	M	T	W	T	F	S	S	M	T	W	T	F	S	S	M	T	W	T	F	S
			1	2	3	4							1				1	2	3	4
5	6	7	8	9	10	11	2	3	4	5	6	7	8	5	6	7	8	9	10	11
12	13	14	15	16	17	18	9	10	11	12	13	14	15	12	13	14	15	16	17	18
19	20	21	22	23	24	25	16	17	18	19	20	21	22	19	20	21	22	23	24	25
26	27	28	29	30	31		23	24	25	26	27	28	29	26	27	28	29	30		
							30	31												

APRIL								AUGUST								DECEMBER						
S	M	T	W	T	F	S	S	M	T	W	T	F	S	S	M	T	W	T	F	S
						1		1	2	3	4	5						1	2
2	3	4	5	6	7	8	6	7	8	9	10	11	12	3	4	5	6	7	8	9
9	10	11	12	13	14	15	13	14	15	16	17	18	19	10	11	12	13	14	15	16
16	17	18	19	20	21	22	20	21	22	23	24	25	26	17	18	19	20	21	22	23
23	24	25	26	27	28	29	27	28	29	30	31			24	25	26	27	28	29	30
30														31						

The Mohammedans don't monkey around. They follow a strict lunar calendar with 12 months, alternating 29 and 30 days, totaling a year of only 354 days. They let the seasons change so that every 32 ½ years they have worked themselves completely through the 4 seasons. It means that every 16 ¼ years they truly have June in January.

There are 14 possible calendar configurations in the Gregorian calendar. Seven of them are 365-day years with the first of January starting on each of the seven days of the week. The other seven types are the same except February 29 is added in each case. The year 1972 is classed as the fourteenth type — a Leap Year calendar of 366 days with the first of January starting on a Saturday. The next time this could happen is in 28 years (7 Leap Year types times 4 years), but — 28 years from now is the year 2000 and according to the Pope's rules, no extra day in that year. So, our year of 1972 is the last one of its type until the year 2028 or 56 years from now. That would make me 110 years old.

I remembered that when I observed Tuesday, February 29, 1972. It was the last one of that kind I'll ever see. Kind of shakes you up, doesn't it?

February, 1972

Part 2

THE SPRING SEASON
March through May

"Little did I realize the barometric pressure would drop an astounding 100 points or more within 60 hours."

A RECORD LOW

My wife is always hard pressed to find something useful as a present for my birthdays so, for the past several, she has asked me what I would like to have. What golden opportunities to fill in some of my long-sought wants, and on my latest birthday not too long ago, she gave me two special recording devices. I now have a week's record of the barometric pressure on one chart and on another chart, the temperature.

Atmospheric pressure has always fascinated me and if you let yourself get too technical, the wonders of it tend to escape you. Just imagine the force creating the everyday winds and breezes — a force that is nothing but air flowing from an area of high pressure to an area of lower pressure. The fact that pressures and wind directions influence our lives is indicated by the following fishing ditty:

When the wind is from the north, useless then to venture forth;

When the wind is from the east, then the fishes bite the least;

When the wind is from the south, blow the bait to the fish's mouth;

When the wind is from the west, then the fishes bite the best.

But then, if you think about pressure, the natural question

to ask is how come there is pressure, and why lows and highs. To me, the easiest way to picture atmospheric pressure is to pretend you're at sea level. Take a hollow square tube one inch on each side and then make it long enough to reach way up to the very top of the atmosphere. The weight of that column of air in that square tube at the bottom or sea level is the atmospheric pressure in pounds per square inch.

If you do the same thing while standing on a Denver street one mile above sea level, there will be less air in that tube because you're higher and the tube is shorter — and the air pressure is therefore less because of the lesser amount of air.

It so happens that water molecules move around faster and faster as they're heated. They are kept contained by air pressure until, at sea level, when the water reaches 212 degrees F., the moving force of the molecules exceeds the air pressure and the molecules escape in wholesale lots as steam. Go back to that Denver street. With less air pressure, the water molecules can escape at a lower temperature or a lower boiling point — exactly 5 degrees F. less or 207 degrees F. Because boiling occurs at a lower temperature, it takes longer to cook food in the mountains.

A barometer is a pressure-measurer. Atmospheric pressure at sea level is 14.7 pounds per square inch on an average day. This weight of air will cause a column of mercury to rise in a tube exactly 29.92 inches. As air pressure drops, so does the mercury up the column. A pressure rise causes a mercury rise. Mercury barometers, and modifications of them, have been common tools for ages and atmospheric pressure is usually expressed as "30.10 and rising" or "29.90 and steady" — referring to the height of the mercury column.

My wife gave me an aneroid barometer. It is a dry barometer composed of a "box" with some air removed. As the air pressure changes, the box expands or contracts, creating a movement that is passed on to a recording arm which in turn draws a line on a chart. The chart is turned by a clock motor and the mark made by the arm is tied exactly to the current time.

Pressure changes occur in the atmosphere with heat and

cold, and dryness and humidity, and because areas affect each other; there are a million complex factors that make up our weather. The lowest barometric pressure ever recorded was during a thunderstorm in the Philippines when it bottomed at 26.18 inches. The heart of a tornado undoubtedly has less pressure than that but it has never been recorded. The measuring equipment never survives!

For our area, a record low of 28.73 inches was set on February 26, 1971. The development of this super-low was interesting.

At 7 A.M., February 24, the barometer read 29.80 and falling. Little did I realize the barometric pressure would drop an astounding 100 points or more within 60 hours.

By the morning of the 25th, the barometer had dropped to 29.59, but it was a nice morning. The sky was clear, the sun pretty as it rose at 6:59 A.M., the wind east at 6 m.p.h. and the temperature a balmy 21 degrees. No dire weather forecasts were being broadcast (it doesn't take much to get them started), but the pressure readings continued to drop slowly all day until reaching 29.46 at 4 P.M. Then, strangely, the pressure started to rise and by midnight was up to 29.50.

Friday's dawn presented a calm foggy view, the temperature was 34 degrees and, in my mind at least, red danger

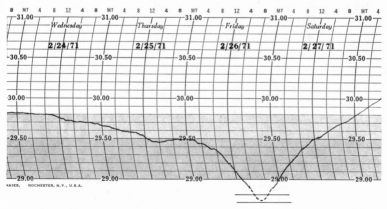

Record Low Barometric Pressure
28.73 at 7:15 PM, 2/26/71

flags were waving. The barometer read 29.38 inches, was falling, and had commenced this fall again by 2 A.M. that day. What was going to happen? I have to admit I was most apprehensive and — shades of the 1941 Armistice Day blizzard! — at about 9:30 A.M. Friday, it started to rain and the graph plainly shows a "jig" in its line when the bright flash of lightning and the great clap of thunder occurred at 11 A.M.

By noon Friday, it was obvious that the stage was set for some sort of very severe weather, especially so with the pressure continuing to drop and at 4 P.M., THE RECORDING NEEDLE WENT RIGHT OFF THE PAPER!

According to the Twin Cities' airport weather bureau, the barometric pressure reached an all-time low for our area of 28.73 inches at 7:50 P.M. Friday, February 26, 1971, two points below the previous record of 28.75 set April 13, 1964, and 85 points lower than the general pressure reading on the day of the 1965 tornado. I estimate that the new record was set at the western edge of Minnetonka at 7:15 P.M.

A mixture of snow and rain was falling, turning to full snow when 10:00 P.M. arrived.

A wild west wind started about then and within an hour, visibility was nil. I appreciate the fact that those people living in the city or in cozy apartments removed from the elements weren't aware of the severe weather, but those who ventured forth in the country know full well how bad it was. For a solid 30 hours, the winds blew with gusts to 60 m.p.h. as the western air piled into the intense low-pressure trough created by the abnormally low barometric reading.

We were extremely lucky to get out of that storm as well as we did. The rain and snow combined for a total of only .72 of an inch of moisture at The Pass, but some snow drifts were five feet thick. In my opinion, we narrowly missed a major disaster.

June, 1970
March, 1971

*"...it reemphasizes the fact that after all, we're
just a tiny speck in a very, very big system."*

THE COMET BENNETT

Every once in a while, something happens which is so
spectacular so interesting and so fascinating that it almost
defies belief that there would be somebody who would not
want to experience it.

I'm referring to the magnificent comet which has been
gracing our sky.

Last Saturday morning (April 4, 1970), I was standing
out on our east deck at 3:30 A.M. — in pajamas, bare feet
and all — totally awestruck by the sight of Bennett's comet
hanging above Island Park just north of the Enchanted
Island bridge on Lake Minnetonka, so beautifully visible
in the northeastern sky about 30 degrees above the horizon.

I had briefly read someplace a short time ago that a new
comet had been discovered last December and would be
visible just about now. So, I set the alarm and decided to
get up early out of curiosity to see for myself.

Well, it may seem like a chore to crawl out of the sack
so early in the morning just to peek at a light in the sky,
but if you do it and the sky is clear, I absolutely guarantee
you it will be an experience you will never forget.

It surpasses eclipses, it brings tears to your eyes and
reemphasizes the fact that after all, we're just a tiny speck
in a very, very big system.

A good visible comet happens every ten years or so,

and then most of them are small or without much of a tail or are very dim — but not this one.

It has everything.

Its nucleus or bright spot in the head may be as large as our earth. The head or cloudy mass around the bright spot could be as much as 100 thousand miles across. The gorgeous tail streaming far behind the head conceivably could be as long as 100 million miles, longer than the distance from our earth to the sun. Those are pretty fancy statistics, but they show the grandeur of the display.

There are a lot of people constantly watching for comets. Most comets haven't appeared before and, therefore, anybody has a good chance of being the one to discover new beauty.

Such was the fortune of John C. Bennett, an amateur watcher of the heavens living in Victoria, South Africa. He had spent 153 hours sweeping the skies for comets during 1969 when, on December 28, he caught a faint haze way out there where there shouldn't be a haze. He immediately announced his find which was confirmed the next night by a station in Australia.

Indeed, there was a new comet coming into view. Comet Bennett (1969I) or the ninth comet discovered during 1969, went into the record books.

So far, little information has been distributed about this comet. It was discovered only a little more than 90 days ago, and it takes time for a mass of information to be gathered, printed and passed around.

It is known, however, that already the comet is losing its brightness or magnitude as it has reached its closest position to the sun and now is receding and growing fainter.

When I first saw it on April 4, it had a magnitude of 2.5, or about the brightness of the stars in the big dipper. By April 16 it will have faded to a 4th magnitude and by April 24, a 5th magnitude — faint enough that it will be difficult to see with the naked eye.

Because comets are relatively rare, there are many misconceptions about their origins, makeup, and behavior. For instance, comets are not "burning up" but rather are

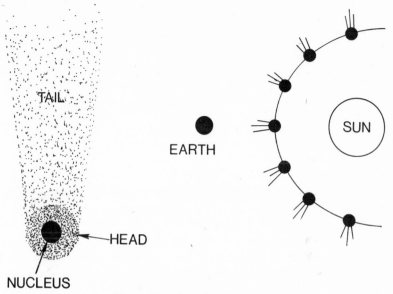

The tail and path of a comet

made of materials that reflect the sunlight when you see them, and also have some glow or luminescence of their own.

As proof of this, several well-known comets, like Halley's, have been known for centuries and show no decrease to speak of in their size or brightness when in view. Also, comets are only seen for two or three hours after sunset or before sunrise because their light has to be reflected sunlight. One theory on comet structure is that they are actually made up of chunks of ices of gases like carbon dioxide, methane and even water, and a hot comet just isn't possible.

All comets have three distinct parts — a nucleus, a head, and a tail. The nucleus is the bright spot in the head and is the mother of the comet, the main body of material from which the head and tail get their stuff. The nucleus is constantly throwing off rocks and sand and gases (don't forget that the nucleus can be as huge as our entire earth), and the cloudy head is the collection around the nucleus of this sloughed-off matter. Some of the head's material overcomes the sun's attraction, or is actually propelled away by streams of atoms from the sun, to form the long streaming tail — always streaming in a direction away from the sun.

Most astronomers agree that comets are a permanent part of the solar system and travel around the sun in varying paths. The closer they are to the sun, the brighter the reflection, but no matter where they are in relation to the sun or how near or far away, their tails always point away from the sun.

Some comets have paths that periodically bring them into view from our earth. One of the most famous is Halley's comet, a spectacle that occurs every 76.3 years, and was first recorded as having been seen in 240 B.C. Edmund Halley was an Englsih astronomer who, in 1682, predicted that a comet that had been reported from time to time through the ages was the same comet and calculated that it would show again in the spring of 1759. It did and was named for him.

It will be visible from earth in 1986. The last time it was seen was in 1910 and our earth actually passed through the tail of the comet without harm except for a great show of meteorites as some of the particles of the tail hit the earth's atmosphere.

The word "comet" is Greek for long hair, and this alone should make Comet Bennett a part of the current scene. But whether you like long hair or not, the sight of a major comet is one that can never be forgotten.

April, 1970

*"...white streaks down their faces...
everywhere...fish slime and the musty
odor of thousands of carp..."*

SEINING FOR CARP

Back in the mid-1880s a fish called the German carp was
introduced to Lake Minnetonka. Lake dwellers have been
living with this fish ever since and will have to continue
to do so unless all fish in the lake are killed off and selected
fish re-introduced. In my opinion, this would be a catas-
trophe for Minnetonka.

The other day I had a delightful lunch with a Department
of Conservation man who lives on the lake, has observed
it for thirty-three years, and has an in-depth knowledge of
the causes and effects of all sorts of things relating to lakes
and the out-of-doors. He agreed with me that carp aren't
nearly as bad as their reputation.

As a matter of fact, he surmises that back in 1880, before
carp were introduced into the lake, the shallower western
and northern bays of Minnetonka were probably choked
with weeds. After the carp came and rapidly multiplied,
their rooting action along the bottom of these shallower
bays resulted in fewer weeds and these bays have been
better for recreational use ever since. In my twenty-two
years of watching Minnetonka, I haven't noticed any increase in the number of carp. Apparently they have struck
a balance and vary little in spite of seining and natural
causes of death.

Carp have been seined for years. My records of hauls

go back to the winter of 1923-24 when more than 68,000 pounds of carp were removed. The next year was the big one with a record 262,285 pounds taken out. Over the years, the catch has been around 70,000 pounds per year. This averages out to about 5.3 pounds of carp per year per acre of lake area.

The two best areas for carp seining on Minnetonka are Halsteds Bay and Smiths Bay, not because there are more carp in these bays, but because they have lake bottom areas that are relatively smooth, free from objects and of a uniform depth to get a good drag with the net.

In recent years, Smiths Bay has been the only place people have seined, as the Halsteds take was getting less and less. Also, a carp trap part way up Six-Mile Creek at the mouth of the lake in the western corner of Halsteds was doing a good job. The crew did try a haul at the west end of Lafayette Bay, got hung up on something, and spent 2½ days getting the net out.

Luckily, I was on hand this year for the year's last haul. The day before, a near-record haul of 34,000 pounds of carp had been seined and promptly picked up by a fish-pond operator from Independence, Missouri, who had earlier successfully bid three cents per pound for the carp. He loaded the live fish into a fancy $45,000 aerated and air-conditioned truck to drive back to Missouri. People pay a per-pound rate to catch the carp from his ponds.

As I stood at the edge of the "net pit" in the ice, I couldn't help but drool at the sight of the beautiful bass, large northerns, and thousands of sunfish and crappies that were returned to the lake from the huge net. Several game wardens carefully removed the game fish with small dip nets and slid the fish back through holes in the ice. The rough fish, carp, bullheads and dogfish were removed.

The largest carp taken by state crews was netted several years ago in Lake Waconia and weighed 48 pounds. Minnetonka's record carp is 25 pounds. At one time a 22-pound female was removed from the trap in Six-Mile Creek — and she had nine pounds of spawn in her. The average large carp from Minnetonka is between 12 and 15 pounds.

Feeding the seine under the ice, and then pulling it in filled with fish, is a tricky business.

If you'll refer to the diagram, rectangular hole "A" is cut in the ice far out into the lake. A 20-foot board with a rope attached to one end is fed into this long hole and pushed along under the ice. At 20-foot intervals, round holes are drilled to handle the board and push it on to the next 20-foot hole. This is done in a circular pattern from both sides of

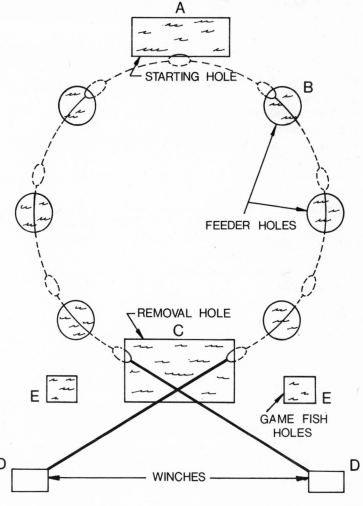

A

STARTING HOLE

B

FEEDER HOLES

REMOVAL HOLE
C

E

E

GAME FISH HOLES

D

D

WINCHES

the original long hole until the board exits at a large rectangular hole cut towards shore. Here, the two ropes crisscross and have their ends attached to winches.

The seining net is attached to the rope at the starting hole out in the lake and fed into the lake. Floats keep the net up against the undersurface of the ice and weights take its bottom down. As the net is drawn in, the fish congregate towards the removal hole. After all game fish are removed, the seining net is hauled onto the ice and the carp harvested.

I have nothing but admiration for the Conservation Department crew. Although the sun may be out and the temperature mild, a brisk wind can make it downright cold on the ice. But they work hour after hour, black rubber suits glistening in the sun, white streaks down their faces where the moisture from watering eyes has evaporated but the body salts remain, seines and nets freezing stiff in seconds, and everyplace water on ice, and snow and fish slime and the musty odor of thousands of carp, and fighting occasional frustration from snags and chains broken while hauling ice blocks out of the big pit where the main seines are concentrated.

Through it all was the smooth-working of a real team, in good humor despite the word from the foreman, Irv Belland, they had to stay late and work Saturday.

The carp don't appreciate the hard work, but we do. I hate to think of the effect on the lake if the hundreds of thousands of pounds of carp that have been removed from the lake were still there.

February, 1968
March, 1969
March, 1970

*"...new words...maybe like 'ploon'
which means to plunder the moon..."*

NEW WORDS FOR OLD SONGS

The melodic praises of the moon and its magical effects on land and love are full of words rhyming with "moon" — spoon, June, tune, boon, loon — but it was in tune with the times to add another word — "soon." For soon, the moon was to be invaded by man — man the magnificent, man the spoiler who can create illusions such as those we've had of the mystical moon but who can also destroy these illusions at the instant of his soft landing.

Over the years that I've casually moon gazed, I've known very little about the moon, regarding it much like a friendly neighbor down the street. What is surprising to me is its closeness to us — "only" about 216,000 miles away at its nearest point to earth. The moon itself is not terribly big, only 2,106 miles in diameter (the earth is nearly four times the size).

Some night when there is a big, beautiful full moon, take a few minutes and step outside to look at the moon through a telescope or a pair of binoculars.

The crater that looks like a belly button in the top center of the moon is Tycho, formed when a meteor smacked the moon ages ago. You can still see how something, apparently rock dust, splattered out from the hole. The larger of the two craters to the right of center is Copernicus, fifty-six miles across. The darker areas on the moon are flat or slightly hilly plains that don't catch and reflect as much sunlight as the higher, and therefore brighter, areas do.

About every 29 ½ days, we have a full moon. When full, it rises around sunset and sets the next morning pretty close to sunrise. The moon is full when we see the full reflection of the sun off the moon — when these two bodies are opposite to each other in the sky in relation to the earth. The thin crescent moon is always seen in the west or after sunset; almost no reflection off the moon is being seen as the moon is almost behind the sun in relation to the earth. (No moon at all is when the moon is behind the sun, as far as we're concerned.)

I think it was in the morning while walking to Margaret Fuller Grade School in Minneapolis (a few years ago!!) that I stopped, sat down on a curb, and watched the eclipse of the sun through a piece of heavily-smoked glass prepared ahead of time at home. This experience, plus Will Rogers' charming the opposition in *A Connecticut Yankee in King Arthur's Court* with the total eclipse of the sun, made me very much aware of both the sun and moon eclipses at an early age.

There is something eerie and ominous about a lunar eclipse. First, it is unusual and the unusual always has more mystery to it than the usual. Second, to have a bright full moon fade away — to slip seemingly behind something in stages — can't help but shake you up. Third, you know the moon will resume its fullness after the eclipse, but yet — there it goes and will it come back?

The bright yellow and white light of the normal full moon is replaced by a strange very dull coppery light of the eclipsed moon as the light of the reflected sunlight off the moon is seen after most of the colors are absorbed by the earth's atmosphere and only reddish rays penetrate. Things just aren't the way they usually are.

There's really no mystery to a lunar eclipse. When the moon is full, the sun and the moon are opposite each other so we see the full reflection of the sun off the moon. That's why a full moon rises in the east as the sun sets in the west. Every once in a while the moon rises in full splendor but

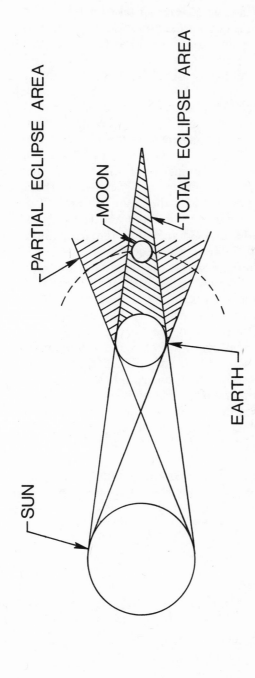

PARTIAL ECLIPSE AREA

MOON

TOTAL ECLIPSE AREA

EARTH

SUN

How a moon eclipse happens

as it continues to rise, its path takes it behind the earth as far as the sun is concerned and the earth interferes with the sun shining on the moon — the earth casts a shadow on the moon, so to speak.

A natural eclipse is magnificent, but a feat to eclipse the eclipse must be what Man has done to land on the moon. After the successful series of Surveyor flights that circled and soft-landed on the moon, the Apollo series that placed Man on the moon must rank as the first-rate achievements that they were. The moon's secrets are slowly being learned — secrets such as temperatures on the moon as high as 1600 degrees at depths up to 700 miles, or that more than 3200 objects crashed onto the moon during 1972 as recorded by sensitive instruments erected and left on the moon.

The first direct evidence that the deep interior of the moon may be molten was received during the summer of 1972. Something large hit the far side of the moon and the compressional waves traveled through the moon to be recorded on instruments on the near side — but the so-called shear waves did not, probably having been absorbed by the liquid core of the moon.

Who can possibly say that there are no more frontiers to conquer, when Man can do such things as land on the moon and be faced with the countless years of research to know and understand our neighbor moon. As new things are learned of the moon, we can keep adding new words for our old moon songs, words maybe like "ploon" which means to plunder the moon or "stoon" which means to stay on the moon.

Let's hope we don't spoil the moon. Let's study it and get to know it, but for heaven's sake, let's live with the moon rather than expect it to live with us.

March, 1968
April, 1972

*"Several red-wing blackbirds chuckled
and chimed....it was a nice morning."*

SPRING IS SPRINGING

The other morning I was awakened at 5:30 A.M. by my
Diamond Dove cooing in the greenhouse. Ordinarily, he is
a very nice quiet bird in the early morn and I was puzzled
as to the cause of this sudden singing — until I heard a
mourning dove outside answering my indoor friend. It was
most pleasant, lying in bed as it grew lighter and the eastern
sky reddened as if blushing with joy in anticipation of
another wonderful day, listening to the bird talk and trying
to imagine what they could be saying to each other.

After breakfast, old Molly and I stood for a long time
on our front deck just looking and listening. The lake ice
was medium gray to black and several brown leaves on the
ice pocked the surface as the dark color absorbed the sun's
heat and hastened the melting under the leaf. The lack of
activity on the lake surface was almost eerie. The ice was
too thick to disappear but too thin and weak to support
snowmobiles or fishermen or skiers or skaters. Even the
dogs were cautious and they left the grayish sheet to a
few crows and grackles around an unusual open spot way
out in the center of the Upper Lake.

With her gray-white muzzle, Molly was an almost perfect
match with the ice in the background as she kept her front
paws on the bench and surveyed the scene. I couldn't help
wonder while watching her if this was perhaps her last

spring and if she ever had thoughts like that. She was born in the spring (on April Fool's Day, when else?) and has always been young at heart.

The lake was silent but nothing else was. Overhead, a male wood duck whistled by, complaining because we were present and he was hungry, while eyeing the golden corn lying on the ice downshore from us. A bluejay called from a far tree. Several redwing blackbirds chuckled and chimed as if mildly scolding us. It was a nice morning.

These past four weeks have been fascinating to watch as the buds thickened on the trees, the birds straggled in, the snow melted, the ice turned from white to gray to black as it became water-soaked, and the screech owls once again took to calling to each other for hours on end during the night. There wasn't even open water along the shore of the Upper Lake when two mallards wheeled by several days ago, closing down to half-throttle as they looked over the corn feeder which obviously was their breakfast table for so many months last year. They liked what they saw and passed the word because the next morning found several of them — and wood ducks — johnny on the spot.

Since I'm still a kid at heart, every spring it's hard for me not to load up with a new puppy or a rabbit or something. (There was a cage full of beautiful rabbits at the Excelsior Farm Store for Easter and I practiced real restraint!) Fortunately, one of my sons has a horse and dogs and cats and ducks and turtles and birds — mixed in with two boys and a patient wife — so I could satisfy my urge for a new pet by getting a two-week-old lamb for my grandson for Easter.

Having this little thing bucking up against the baby bottle (a poor substitute for his mother, who died during his birth) brought back a flood of memories to me. It was June of 1935 that I adopted a tiny lamb cast off by her mother as a huge flock passed through a desolate area in the oil fields of Montana. I named her Nellie and she was a marvelous pet for a somewhat lonesome teenager that summer. As I remember it, the only drawback to the lamb living with me was the noise during the night of her sharp hoofs

Molly looks things over

clattering on the slippery linoleum floor.

Spring is springing, all right. The lake ice may not be out, but my cool-weather garden is in — including peas, radishes, beets, bibb and leaf lettuce, and onions. Eleven American mergansers flew over three days ago and three red-breasted mergansers played around in a little open water between two huge ice floes of the Upper Lake. Crocus, scilla, and snow drops are blooming, and big fat hyacinth buds should pop any day now. My pink French pussy willows in the damp back corner of the woods are plump and fuzzy, the gold of the weeping willow branches shimmer in the sun, and the deep-red of the dogwood shoots is evidence of the leaves to come with their white pattern against the soft green.

One of the ugly sights of spring is the mess by our highways materializing from the melting snow.

I'm tempted to take a can and bottle survey along our lake roads. It's a sorry sight to see the array of boxes, papers, cans, and bottles that show up as the snow leaves the ditches and shoulders. What kind of a person is it who has no thoughts of others and dumps his trash on public property? Who empties the booze bottle, which is bad enough while driving around, and then ejects it out of an open window for all the world to see? Its brown glass stark against the white snow adds one more stain against mankind. Perhaps this is one justification for some day fingerprinting our populace and then laying it to those whose fingerprints are found on the cans and bottles. I'll bet our roadsides would be cleaner for it. (Although I hate the idea of the mass fingerprinting.)

One of the prettiest sights of this spring was the full moon of the other evening rising over the dark, dark lake ice with occasional ribbons and pools of yellow reflecting off water here and there. This kind of sight is not one you can plan to see or would think of seeing, but one you don't forget once you've seen it.

The rebirth of so much of nature that occurs during our springtime has to be something sorely missed by those who live to the south and can't have the swinging of seasons so enjoyed by us. I feel sorry for them — but then, I'm sure they felt sorry for us not so long ago when the wind was wild and snow filled the air and spring seemed so far away.

It has come, though.

April, 1971
April, 1972

*"...of the solar radiation available, clear ice
transmits 84 percent, but two inches of snow
on the ice transmits only 1 percent."*

ICE-OUT IS IN

Last Sunday's hot sun, blue sky, and water collecting in the
footprints in the snow on the ice were omens of spring things
to come. Winter is on its last legs. However, no matter how
high the temperature, how clear the sky or what the date is,
winter still reigns as long as the ice is on the lake. No matter
how cold the day, how gray the sky or how early the month,
spring is here when the ice leaves the lake.

Along with football jackpots in the fall, poker and gin
rummy games in the winter and, for some, bets with your
wife as to what the next baby is going to be, a popular
pastime around our local lake area is to try to figure out
when the ice will go out. It's the "in" thing to do.

Just when the ice will go out depends on several things
that make it impossible to predict. However, long-term
records show that chances are the ice will go out earlier
and earlier. Various records prove that, in our general area,
there are shorter periods of ice cover during the twentieth
century than the nineteenth century. And then there are
Swiss records that go back to 1400 A.D. which document
that the world is getting warmer and the periods of ice cover
on lakes are getting shorter and shorter. There were eight
times in both the fifteenth and sixteenth centuries with
abnormally long ice cover on the lakes. In the seventeenth
and eighteenth centuries, there were six times of unusually

long cover. Come the nineteenth century and we find only four times of such special duration of ice.

Many factors influence the melting of ice. The main ones are: type of ice; depth of ice; depth of water to the bottom; type of water; time of season because of angle of sun's rays and length of day; wind force; number of clear days; amount of snow on the ice; frequency of rain and its temperature; and, last but not least, the natural laws of light and heat, and the properties of water. Besides these natural laws, I think the most important factor is snow on the ice.

Our seasons, our ice, our summer water temperatures, and all things depend upon solar radiation. As the sun dips and dives and changes its path of travel from season to season, the angles at which the sun's rays strike the earth's surface vary and therefore the effects of these rays vary. Added to this is the time of daylight during which these rays can strike any certain surface. In December in our area, our days are the shortest (about 8 hours, 45 minutes of daylight) and solar radiation strikes the earth at its lowest angle because the sun is low, so lots of it skips off. The result is cold weather, ice and snow.

Late March and early April are something else again. The length of daylight is about 12 hours, 45 minutes or 50 percent more daylight than in December and the sun's path is higher with its rays striking the earth's surface at a much more direct angle for better penetration. The result is that rapid warming and melting of the ice is possible at this time of year if other factors allow it.

These other factors include the number of cloudy and clear days and, most important, the amount of snow on the ice. Snow is white because it reflects most of the light that hits it, and therefore the layer of snow prevents solar radiation striking the lake surface from entering and warming the ice. As proof, look at these figures: Of the solar radiation available, clear ice transmits 84 percent, but two inches of snow on the ice transmits only 1 percent. It is estimated that 53 percent of the solar radiation that does enter ice and water is transformed into heat within 3-1/3 feet. Fifty-three percent of clear ice's 84 percent can be a lot of

MARCH				
27	**28**	**29**	1945 **30**	**31**
APRIL 1889 1902 1911 1968 **1**	1905 1946 **2**	1921 **3**	1942 1966 1973 **4**	1895 1896 1930 **5**
1919 1931 **6**	1925 1929 1935 **7**	1907 1953 **8**	1894 1938 1967 **9**	1934 1959 1963 **10**
1892 1948 1958 **11**	1908 1927 1943 1954 1955 **12**	1903 1912 1949 1964 **13**	1887 1918 1932 1941 1961 **14**	**15**
1890 1900 1906 1960 **16**	1914 1915 1920 1922 1939 1969 1971 **17**	1897 1898 1913 1917 1926 1928 1933 **18**	1916 1937 1947 1970 **19**	1936 1957 **20**
1891 1956 **21**	1952 **22**	1901 1923 1944 **23**	1899 1924 **24**	1888 1904 1940 1962 **25**
1909 1972 **26**	**27**	1893 1951 **28**	**29**	**30**
MAY 1965 **1**	1950 **2**	**3**	**4**	1857✳ **5**

✳ FROM OLD LETTER

Lake Minnetonka official ice-out dates, 1887-1973

heat; 53 percent of the 1 percent allowed by two inches of snow is darn near nothing. Lake ice will stay around a long time if protected by snow.

I tested this conclusion on historical ice-out dates for our lake compared to the amount of precipitation for their related months of March. Between 1914 and 1970, seventeen years had ice-out dates on April 10 or before and thirteen years had dates of April 20 or later. These later years averaged 60 percent more precipitation (and more snow) than the earlier group of years. The earlier group contained the six lowest March amounts of precipitation for the period 1914-1970 and the later group contained the four highest amounts. In my opinion, it is no coincidence that these precipitation facts relate to the ice-out dates.

Ice on the lake melts as the days get warmer and longer; the angle of the sun striking the ice becomes higher and therefore the heat rays penetrate further. As these sun rays go through the ice, they warm the water just under the ice. Shallow areas, along the shores and in ponds, melt first because there isn't as much cold water under the ice to cool the warmed-up water.

In the process of melting, the hydrogen and oxygen atoms of the ice molecule scramble back into the more compact arrangement of water. The whitish-looking ice turns to gray as its hexagonal crystals have their impure and lower-melting-point-centers filled with water; the pure walls of the crystals survive until the last minute as "honeycombed ice." Unless a high wind breaks up the gray ice, the ice cover on the lake will all-of-a-sudden seem to sink and the lake is free once again. What really happens is that the ice crystals tip over on their sides so very little of the crystal is exposed to view, as final melting occurs. It just seems like the ice has sunk.

I like the ice cover on the lake but I like the first view of open water, too. When the ice does go, notice how quickly — like immediately — the loons, mergansers, ducks, coots, and herring gulls show up.

They like the open water, too.

April, 1971

A LOST JURION-GROOTER CROSS

The telephone rang and it was a friend calling from over on Smithtown Bay with the news that a tuckered-out pigeon had been picked up and was resting comfortably in their basement, safe from the wild winds and extreme cold of the outside. On its legs were three sets of bands, but nothing could be deciphered from them. Would I help?

A day later, I arrived at their house with a large cage from my garage. I took the bird to my office. By now, my secretaries and everybody else are not surprised at anything that I bring. They've seen wood duck eggs incubating in engineering, red squirrels in Hav-A-Hart traps sitting by the receptionist, and odd-looking water samples by the dozens waiting to be picked up or having just been delivered. So, what's new about a pigeon sitting in Mr. Gray's office?

When I used a lighted, large magnifying glass, one leg band yielded "AU69Mpls13793," a second band was merely a plastic yellow and blue-coded identification strip, and the third band gave the name and address of the owner. A quick phone call and we were in business.

The pigeon was a very nice fellow, no noise and a clean bird. He (as it turned out to be) was a dapper thing with a royal stance and obviously of better breeding that a common street pigeon. When his owner arrived to pick him up the next morning, I learned that the pigeon's grandmother and grandfather had come from Cromwell, England, and he was called a Red Check from his pattern and coloration. He was a racing pigeon and was technically a Jurion-Grooter Cross. Jurion was an English breeder, as was Grooter, whose strain had been highly developed by an American, C. D. Fisher. Fisher is now eighty-one years old and friends have said he was born with a pigeon in his mouth, instead of a silver spoon.

The pigeon owner has 150 birds and belongs to the Minneapolis Racing Pigeon Club, one of seven such clubs in our metro area. Our lost friend was one of his good breeders who hadn't been racing lately and became lost because the owner had changed houses since the bird had last flown. To make matters very confusing for the bird, the old house had been torn down. He apparently returned to find no house and then wandered for several days before landing by Lake Minnetonka. His real home is many miles northeast, in Champlin.

These pigeons are homing, carrier, racing pigeons, and are specially bred pigeons from the general bird order of Columbiformes of two families and 302 species. Egyptians used pigeons to carry messages as far back as 3000 B.C., Julius Caesar used them in battle and they are still being used in Vietnam. Pigeons have a very strong homing instinct and selective breeding has sharpened it even more. The most famous carrier pigeon was named Kaiser and lived to be 25 years old while flying for the U.S. Army.

Our pigeon owner has a yearling champion, a red check hen who last year won a 440-mile race from Topeka, Kansas, to Osseo, Minnesota, and then, the very next weekend, set a record. The bird was flown to Tulsa, Oklahoma, where it was released at 5:40 A.M. and arrived home at 8:35 P.M. the same day — flying a distance of 640 miles in 15 hours non-stop without food or water.

These racing pigeons are very clean birds (unlike the average street pigeon) and transmit no human disease. After mating, the female takes 10 days to lay two eggs. They hatch in 17 to 18 days and within four weeks the young are standing outside the loft getting the lay of the land. After they

A racing pigeon fitted with a tracking device

start to fly, they are taken farther and farther away from home to develop their wing muscles and hone the homing instinct. A racing pigeon normally flies at from 40 to 45 miles per hour with from 4 to 8 wing-beats per second. Their short, muscular wings make them strong flyers but lousy gliders.

A pigeon race can be long or short. For short races, pigeons are trucked to the starting point with as many as 27 crates of 30 birds each (that's 800 birds in a race). Long races have the birds sent by commercial air and cooperating clubs receive the birds, feed and water them, and then release them when weather conditions are right. Pigeons can't fly in heavy rain as they get water-logged, so weather systems are watched carefully. Once a town literally rained pigeons when a large race ran into a thunderstorm overhead, and live and dead wet pigeons were everyplace in town.

When racing, the birds hug the ground where the air resistance is the least, and then fly up and over fences, trees, and the like. Many is the time birds arrive home with broken legs and wings, or split-open breasts from flying into barbed wire fences. Some collapse and die once they get home. Nobody can really explain the strong homing instinct of birds in general and pigeons in particular. But even starlings have it. In Germany, some starlings were taken by train to a town 93 miles away and, while in transit, were rotated on a phonograph turntable 5,000 times. When released, they returned directly home.

Some of our great homo sapiens can't even read a road map.

March, 1972

*"...they tugged and dipped and filled the sky
with colors and motion — much like balloons
at the kickoff of a Minnesota homecoming
football game."*

KITE SIGHTS

The gayest occasion for kite-flying that I've experienced
happened on the island of Bermuda several years ago on
Easter morning. The residents have the delightful custom
of celebrating the arising of Christ by having kite contests
Easter morning. For generations, fathers have taught sons
how to make special kites with the distinctive colors and
shapes that each family has developed. Our family gathered
this one special Easter on a high hill that fell sharply to the
sea. We became part of the festivities by watching the kites
being assembled, helping get them airborne, and then having
the thrill of playing some of them while they tugged and
dipped and filled the sky with colors and motion — much
like balloons at the kickoff of a Minnesota homecoming
football game.

I love kites. Those of you who have been outside this
winter near The Pass have probably seen my big yellow
and blue cloth bird kite gaily fluttering high in the sky at
the end of a thousand feet of nylon string. Over the years,
I've had many a kite, usually of the ten-cent variety from
the drug store made with tissue paper and thin sticks. About
a year ago, I read in the *New York Times* about a new store
in New York — the Go-Fly-A-Kite store — that sells nothing
but kites and their supplies. I visited this store a few months
ago and bought the cloth kite.

It is of a special design, done by a friend of the East Indian who owns the Manhattan store. It goes up in the slightest breeze and is steady as a rock in the sky, even without a tail.

Just who invented the kite is open to question. Some say the Greeks in 400 B.C., some say the Chinese in 200 B.C., but I've always had the feeling that the Chinese have used the kites the most and still make a big deal of them. They have a Kite Day which is on the ninth day of the ninth month, and I've seen pictures of the Chinese sky literally filled with kites. They believe a kite floats away any evil spirits.

The month of March is known as kite month because of the strong and steady winds, but there's no reason not to extend the kite season into April or the year around for that matter. Maybe someday we can get more people around here to fly more kits on Easter and develop the interest in kite flying that is present in so many other locations.

I visited one of these "locations" a few weeks ago while in Florida and discovered not only a new kind of kite, but also a whole new principle of flight. For two hours during a late afternoon in Boca Raton with the wind brisk, the sky a sunny blue, and the company fascinating, I "flew" several sizes of multi-colored kites that didn't look like kites and were called aero-sleds. The largest had an area of 45 square feet, and using line nearly 1/16 inch thick in a 15 m.p.h. breeze, I found myself with heels dug into the ground and arms tired to the very seams after ten minutes of playing with this spectacular thing officially called a "Jalbert Airfoil." The principle was perfected and the first flight made in March 1963. These kites have a phenomenal load-carrying ability.

In 1883, an Englishman named Douglas Archibald flew a kite with an anemometer or wind instrument 1,200 feet up. In 1890, William Eddy of Bayonne, New Jersey, invented the Eddy Bow kite, which is the common cheap paper kite of today. The box-kite was invented in 1893 by an Australian, Lawrence Hargrave, to carry a heavy load of self-recording meterological instruments. Marconi used a kite in 1894 to elevate an antenna to receive the first trans-Atlantic radio signals, and during World War II, kites were widely used

The new Jalbert kite design

to fly radar reflectors and gunnery targets.

Kites get their lift or ability to fly by taking advantage of the aerodynamic force of the wind upon their surfaces. For a person to invent a new kind of kite requires a thorough background of flight and its principles — and Domina C. Jalbert, the "Jalbert Airfoil" inventor, is no exception. He was with me that day I flew the aero-sleds in Florida and, even though he is totally professional and has flown thousands of kites thousands of hours, he was still like a kid, running across the open field picking up sand burrs on his socks while checking out a newly-made airfoil that was due to be shipped to Israel for high-altitude instrument work.

These Jalbert airfoils don't look like kites because they really are a totally new kind of kite. Actually, they are wings which become inflated by the wind pressure and act like sleds coasting against the wind when in the air. My $35 "Robin" is an ingenious combination of an airplane wing, a barrage balloon, a kite as we know them, and a special parachute rigging that gives a multiple center of effort for great stability. It weighs only half a pound and folds up into a pack five inches square and two inches thick, but when flying it has an area of 13 square feet and exerts a pull of 32 ½ pounds in a 30 m.p.h. wind. It has no rigid members and gets its strength from the heatset nylon material used in the construction. I fly the "Robin" using a 90-pound test nylon line. My first effort two weeks ago almost ended in losing everything as I let out 1,000 feet of line in a 20 m.p.h. wind not realizing what terrific pull would result. I finally had to let go, unhappily watching my new purchase disappearing over the trees to the south. It was recovered after chasing it by snowmobile and finding it on the ice a half-mile away.

A neighbor of mine suggested I buy a stiff deep-sea fishing rod with a big reel that includes a gear ratio for controlling the flight of the aero-sled. I can imagine the look on somebody's face if they see me with a salt-water rod on Minnetonka. If they ask me what I'm doing, I'll say I'm flying a Robin in the sky instead of snagging a kingfish in the sea.

April, 1969
April, 1971

"...10 mallard ducklings...arrived by parcel post
...from the first hour, they never trusted me."

SPRING DUCK BEHAVIOR

One of my favorite books is *King Solomon's Ring* by Konrad Lorenz. The book's name is derived from a tale that King Solomon, son of David in the Holy Scriptures, had a magic ring that made it possible for him to talk with the birds and animals. The author has put together a book that is full of stories of his associations with birds and animals. He is convinced that he himself can communicate with the beasts.

To a certain extent, I feel I can communicate with our wild and domesticated friends, not necessarily by language or such means, but rather by a depth of feeling for them which rubs off. Somehow or other, they just know I like them and won't hurt them.

Last spring, ten mallard ducklings put my personal theory to test and I nearly lost faith in myself. One of my sons and I shared a purchase from Sears Roebuck of a box of day-old mallards that arrived by parcel post at 9:30 P.M. at the post office and had to be picked up right away. My share of the box was the ten little things, and I was looking forward to having them adopt me, follow me around all summer long, and come swooping over our big deck at lakeside when called and when they knew the corn was ready.

From the first hour, they never trusted me. While still tiny, they would huddle in the corner of the big pen, wild and spooky and not at all like the friendly little ducks I had in mind. This bothered me because I'd seen pictures, as you have, of ducks trailing after a human across a road or through a field. So, back to the books I went, and two simple things came to light that explain the trouble. One is that even a partially-domesticated duck has a behavior entirely different from a truly wild duck, and I had wild ducks. Secondly, a tiny duck, especially when wild, will relate to almost anything as long as the thing is on all fours. This explains why they tag after dogs and, to a certain extent, why they will follow a small child more often than a tall man because the child is closer to the ground.

I found a perfect example of the "all-fours" association in a story in *King Solomon's Ring*. The author had the trouble I had, getting young mallards to "track," so he learned the young peep and spent weeks crawling around on his hands and knees. They followed him with no strain but, no matter how familiar they became with him, the instant he stood upright, they would scatter.

Another behavioral characteristic of mallards which is occurring right now, and one you probably have seen time and again, is the "three-bird flight." What this amounts to is that a mallard drake has staked out a territory for breeding with his girl friend and then, along comes another pair. He rises to challenge them and the chase is on. Time and again this happens in the spring and always involves two drakes and a hen. Sometimes the protecting drake will actually grab the tail feathers of the hen in flight and pull her to the ground. I've seen this happen and, from the ground, it looks terribly confusing up there. Reactions of birds in flight are so fast. Just watching the mallards during a "three-birder" shows the amazing grace with which one bird can exactly follow the intricate path of flight of another. Their powers of anticipation must be great.

A friend of mine is a professor in the Ecology and Behavioral Biology Department at the University of Minnesota and he's an expert on duck behavior. He wrote a very learned report for the Wildfowl Trust in 1965 on the chasing that goes on between ducks and how this relates to the spacing that occurs in nesting areas. A wonderful book

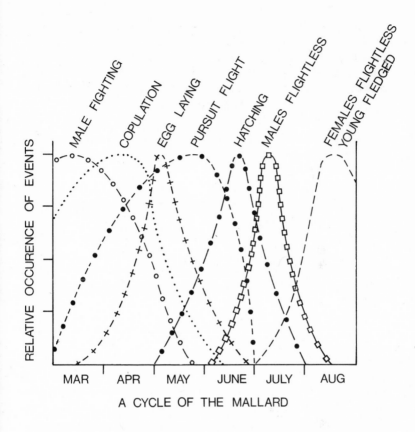

MALE FIGHTING

COPULATION

EGG LAYING

PURSUIT FLIGHT

HATCHING

MALES FLIGHTLESS

FEMALES FLIGHTLESS
YOUNG FLEDGED

RELATIVE OCCURENCE OF EVENTS

MAR   APR   MAY   JUNE   JULY   AUG

A CYCLE OF THE MALLARD

called *Waterfowl, Their Biology and Natural History* by
Johnsgard, published by the University of Nebraska Press,
has a chart that graphs the seasonal events of the mallard,
based upon ducks observed in northern Europe, southern
Canada, and the northern United States.

The accompanying graph is an enlarged and simplified
portion of the chart from this book and shows some of the
things that happen to a mallard for the six-month period of
March through August. There are two or three interesting
things that make for interesting watching. "Three-bird" pursuit flights will continue as a common occurrence until
about June 1, then fall off sharply. Early in July, the drakes
start moulting and for a while are flightless. By mid-August,

the hens are flightless and take to the air again just when the young have their wing-feathers developing to the point that they can consider flight.

Keep your eyes peeled for these mallard antics. It's fun to watch them, but even more fun when you understand a little of what is happening and why.

That goes for all things.

April, 1971

"I hope we all realize that rabbits don't lay eggs,
but it is true that rabbits come from eggs,
as does all animal life..."

EASTER AND EGGS

It's a surprising fact that Easter Sunday can vary in dates over a span of 35 days. This year, with Easter landing on April 2, it has to be regarded as early because the average date is around April 7 or 8.

Way back in A.D. 325, the first Nicene Council of the Nicaea area in Asia Minor declared that Easter Sunday would be the first Sunday after the first full moon on or after March 21. By this formula, the earliest that Easter can ever be is March 22 and the latest is April 25. Easter was on March 22 in 1761, then in 1818, but won't fall on that date again until sometime in the 22nd century. In 1943, Easter was on April 25, but that won't happen again until the year 2038.

Between 1972 and the year 2000, Easter will occur in April 23 times and March only 6 times. In 1973 (and in 1984), Easter will be very late — April 22 — but will be early — March 26 — in 1978 and again in 1989.

Christians celebrate Easter as a commemoration to the resurrection of Christ, following Good Friday or the day of Christ's crucifixion (Mohammedans say Adam was created on Good Friday). Others regard Easter as the time of birth or spring or the coming of light. The name Easter comes from the Anglo-Saxon goddess Eostre, meaning light or spring. However, nearly everybody regards eggs as a part of Easter and a sign of new life, and the use of eggs at Eastertime goes back to early customs in Egypt and Persia.

One legend has it that the bunny rabbit lays eggs on Easter eve and the eggs must be hunted and found the next morning. I hope we all realize that rabbits don't lay eggs, but it is true that rabbits come from eggs, as does all animal life with the exception of the most primitive of forms. Eggs are the way of reproduction. We come from eggs, earthworms lay eggs, one oyster can produce 500,000,000 (yes, five hundred million) eggs, a sturgeon 7,000,000, and a carp at least 2,000,000.

In general, eggs lead the way to reproduction by hatching either internally, like us, or externally, like the birds. Those eggs that develop and hatch externally are nearly always larger because the egg must contain moisture and food for the embryo during development, independent from the mother's body.

Bird eggs are marvelous things and like most other things, they vary in size and shape and color. Most eggs are roundish or oblong, and colors usually are white to blue to brown to green, and speckled. In size, they range from the minute little things of the hummingbird to the monsters of the ostrich. The hornbill bird lays only one egg per year, whereas a good laying leghorn chicken will lay as many as 350 full-sized eggs in a year.

Chicken eggs are the common Easter eggs in America and around the world and are a good buy this year (1972), because of a severe over-production, caused by too many chickens as a result of new medications that have drastically reduced the usual chicken mortality. A quick telephone check confirmed that the present price on the New York market for the average egg is 36 cents per dozen. The farmer is usually paid 6 cents a dozen under the wholesale market price, which means 30 cents a dozen or 2 ½ cents per egg. I would guess that hardly covers the cost of feed.

A recent bill in Congress, defeated early this week, called for a henocide or the slaughter of millions and millions of chickens to stabilize the egg market and drive prices up. However, nature is stepping in. In Southern California, the

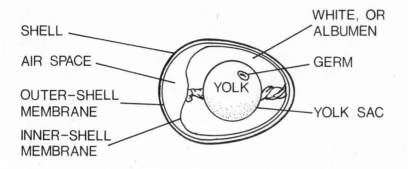

SHELL

AIR SPACE

OUTER-SHELL MEMBRANE

INNER-SHELL MEMBRANE

YOLK

WHITE, OR ALBUMEN

GERM

YOLK SAC

Cross section of an egg

Asiatic Newcastle disease has already made it necessary to kill 450,000 chickens and another 1.4 million are ticketed for destruction. This disease, which showed up in late 1970 and early 1971, was brought into the state by pet birds from South America and Asia. The best means of combating the disease to date is to remove whole flocks and upwards of $500 million worth of birds are threatened. By the way, there are 25 million laying hens just in Southern California.

A chicken egg by weight is 58 percent white, 31 percent yoke, and 11 percent shell. The shell is pure carbonate of lime and the inside of the egg is 74 percent ash. The white of an egg alone is 86 percent water.

Eggs that we usually buy are infertile eggs and won't hatch, but several of the Nature Food stores around town and on the campus carry fertile eggs. If you are going to dye Easter eggs, and if you use fertile eggs, please realize that the egg will know not only when you dip the egg into hot water but also that you're going to do it.

Don't laugh. A man by the name of Backster discovered a phenomenon quite by accident in 1969 and is shaking up the scientific world. One of his experiments was to wire up a fertile egg in its earliest stage of development to record via electrical impulses reactions to things affecting the egg.

He found that one egg will go into a tizzy when another egg is broken in its presence. When examining the unbroken egg, he could find no physical or circulatory structure that could possibly account for the impulses he recorded.

So here we go, finding that eggs may have personalities. It won't be long, I suppose, before we can truly say, "He's a good egg" or "He's a bad egg." In the meantime, dye those Easter eggs. And if you're the timid type, turn your head when you dip the egg into the hot water.

March, 1972

"...he decided to experiment with the plant by burning a leaf with a match. At the instant he DECIDED to do it, the plant showed a violent reaction..."

BACKING BACKSTER

Some are saying that science is being thrown a real curve. Others are saying that along with Newton and his apple, Darwin and his apes, and the Wright brothers and their airplane, Cleve Backster and his charts will take a most respected place in scientific history.

Last week in my column on Easter eggs, I mentioned Backster and his experiments with eggs, showing that fertile eggs seem to be highly sensitive to some things and actually show severe reactions. Many have asked me about that — so, here's some information on the Backster Phenomenon and how it developed. It's new.

Cleve Backster is an expert with the lie detector or polygraph. He has been with the CIA (Central Intelligence Agency) and has operated his own school in New York to train law enforcement officers in the use of the lie detector. This polygraph prints out on a chart the PGR or psycho-galvanic reflex of a subject that is wired to a small electrical circuit. Responses to things can be measured on the chart which moves at the rate of six inches per minute and these responses end up as a line drawn on the chart. An expert can interpret the motion of the line in relation to the reactions of the subject to questions or to certain stimuli.

Judging from his picture, Backster is in early middle-age with a real crew-cut burr-head. He probably has a beard that I'm sure gives a 5 o'clock shadow at noon, a very square jaw, and arms as hairy as Burt Reynold's Cosmopolitan chest. He loves plants and animals.

On the possibly-historic day of February 2, 1966, Backster was watering a plant — a dracaena masangeana, in case you're interested — and decided to hook up his polygraph wires to the plant to see if he could tell how fast the plant absorbed the new water. The result was that he received a chart reading that couldn't be related to water absorption and he started to ponder as to what could have caused the reaction. At exactly 13 minutes 55 seconds of chart time, he decided to experiment with the plant by burning a leaf with a match. At the instant he DECIDED to do it, the plant showed a violent reaction — and he was off and running into a new area of science that many have said is "an extension of our natural laws."

In 1969, National Wildlife Magazine published an article about his experiments and seven thousand scientists around the world contacted him. Since then, he's been famous, and recently another article in the same magazine told about more of his work, including the egg experiments.

Three basic things about plants have come to the surface with the Backster Phenomenon: (1) plants seem to be highly sensitive to people; (2) plants seem to be highly sensitive to destruction of any form of animal life; and (3) plants seem to be very sensitive to threats to their own existence. Further work is proving similar conclusions regarding all living matter.

What appears to be happening is that living cells broadcast signals, and the strongest signals come when apprehension and distress are involved. Even the most basic or primary of cells do it with no pattern relating to their biological function. All types of cells do it: amoeba, fresh fruit, yeast, blood samples, and even scrapings from a human's mouth. These signals even penetrate through lead-lined containers and don't seem to fall within any known "electro-dynamic spectrum". The signals are not AM or FM or of any other known frequency. Distance is no factor; they have been proven to travel hundreds of miles. Backster

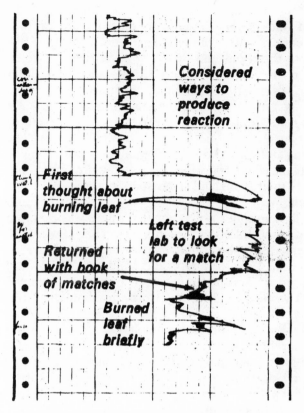

Considered
ways to
produce
reaction

First
thought about
burning leaf

Left test
lab to look
for a match

Returned
with book
of matches

Burned
leaf
briefly

Backster's initial plant polygraph chart

wants to send one of his "friendly" plants to Mars in one
of the probes, and he's positive he can get signals that
travel at twice the speed of any known signal, including
radio waves which take from 6 to 6½ minutes to travel
from Mars to Earth.

At the risk of simplification, here are a few examples
of experiments with plants. He put plants in separate and
closed rooms, and then in another room he dumped live
shrimp into boiling water. Every plant reacted to the shrimp
killing at exactly the same time as the shrimp hit the water.

He put two plants in a room and had six students enter
the room. Backster didn't know which one, but he had

asked one of the students to destroy one of the plants. Thereafter, when the student who destroyed the plant entered the room, the surviving plant reacted violently but gave no reaction when any of the other five entered the room. It's possible plants have memory.

Many groups in high schools around the country have proven the following: take two plants and divide the class into two groups, one for each plant. Have one group do nothing but talk about their plant in a criticizing way and that plant will do poorly and probably die. The other group praises their plant and it prospers by growing in leaps and bounds.

A photographer for National Wildlife was taking pictures of some of Backster's plants and charts when Backster suddenly asked him what was wrong. A plant was showing a reaction of consternation and sympathy. The photographer admitted he had just discovered one of his camera lenses wasn't working and he was worrying about the pictures he had taken.

The Backster Phenomenon has a long way to go and innumerable things to be explained, but there doesn't seem to be any doubt that something is happening — something new and startling. There seems to be the possibility of super signals between man and plants, or any living thing with any other living thing.

I saw a bumper sticker the other day that read "Mankind is One." That's wrong; it should be "Nature is One."

April, 1972

"...the bird is so dependent upon man....
The Martin can be used as an indicator of
change, much like the canary (in the coal mine)."

MARTINS AND MAN

Before the development of special instruments to detect lethal gases in coal mines, a canary in a cage was a constant companion to coal miners. Not only was the canary a nice thing to have around, a welcome reminder that there was an outdoors even though most miners' lives were spent underground, but the sensitivity to minute amounts of poisonous gases caused the canary to die. They served as an early warning to the workers of the impending danger to themselves.

Now, an assistant professor of zoology at Mississippi State University has come up with a unique idea based on somewhat the same principle. He uses the purple martin. He reasons that the martin is widespread in the United States and, almost without exception, his mating houses are man-made, causing the bird to be almost totally dependent upon man. If the bird is so dependent upon man, then any changes in man or changes caused by man will cause a change in the martin habits and population. The martin can be used as an indicator of change, much like the canary.

Starting in April 1971, Jerome Jackson made a survey on purple martins for people who were attending a joint meeting of the Mississippi Ornithological Society and the Oktibbeha Chapter of the National Audubon Society in Starkville, Mississippi. The University news service picked up the survey and distributed it. Within a week, Jackson was receiving a hundred letters a day. A Dr. James Tate Jr. of the Cornell University Laboratory of Ornithology in Ithaca, New York, heard about it and the two men have joined forces in a massive survey attempt to find out more about the martin.

I received a copy of the survey in response to a general letter that I had answered, and a report for the year 1971 shows some remarkable things. First of all, surveys were received from thirty-two states and five Canadian provinces. Minnesota contributed eighteen surveys while Wisconsin sent in eight. North Dakota was good for one.

Of the various surveys received, a total of 23,391 martin apartments were accounted for, inhabited by 17,199 martins or a martin-apartment ratio of .73. Wisconsin had 286 apartments with 164 birds for a ratio of .57 while Minnesota was way down the list with 418 apartments but only 157 birds for a ratio of .38. This is about the same ratio that I experienced in the Minnetonka area.

Why should the ratios vary? Are there more birds per apartments available in some areas than in others? Do populations vary widely from one year to the next and from one area to the next?

Martins have always loved gourds for houses, especially in the south. So far the surveys show that martins prefer gourds to apartment houses, especially when a lot of sparrows are present. Sparrows don't prefer gourds. Therefore. the martins tend to use more gourds than apartments because of the sparrows. Right? That's one question of many to be answered.

Certainly, competition for houses from other birds affect the martins' ability to fill up a house. Surveys from Mississippi showed that of 13,133 apartments, there were 10,797 martins, 1,754 sparrows, and 379 starlings. I have had only one pair of starlings attempt to set up shop in one of my houses (the attempt was short-lived, as were they), but sparrows have always given my martins the fits. I have finally just left the sparrows and martins to their own devices to fight it out.

Purple Martin with a Dragonfly

Something else is being discovered: martins don't eat particularly huge numbers of mosquitoes. A martin house manufacturer claims a bird can eat as many as two thousand mosquitoes a day. This can't be true. Recent stomach counts in martins show that mosquitoes make up a very small part, if any, of the bird's diet. Roberts' *Birds of Minnesota* says that martins eat ants, wasps, drone honey bees, daddy-long-legs, horse flies, bugs, beetles, moths, dragonflies, and spiders; no mention of mosquitoes.

If you wish to help in the purple martin survey, send money to Mississippi State University Development Foundation, Purple Martin Research, Box 423, State College, Mississippi 39762. Or if you want a survey, write Dr. Jerome A. Jackson, Department of Zoology, Mississippi State University, State College, Mississippi 39762. Your contributions are tax deductible, by the way.

We'll lose our martins pretty soon. I find that they leave their houses late in July and spend several weeks in huge flocks before leaving for good. One year they left us early in August. In 1970, it was August 24. One man in Litchfield, Minnesota, says they always leave his area either August 24 or 25. In 1923, however, they left on August 10. Roberts says the average in the Twin City area is between August 28 and September 15. I think that's too late, according to my records. But, in any event, it won't be long and they'll be gone. I will miss them and will wait patiently for next spring. Mid-to-late April is the usual arrival time.

April, 1972
August, 1972

HOUSES FOR THE BIRDS

For years, Wendell Brown preached the fact that "It's fun to have the birds around" and so right he was. It's one thing to have the year-around birds with us, like cardinals, chickadees, nuthatches, bluejays, crows, goldfinches and sparrows (to mention just a few), but it's especially pleasing to be able to attract the spring, summer and fall birds. Aside from those that pass through, the best way to get them for the season is to have homes for them to rent.

Late winter is a good time to build or buy birdhouses and set them out in anticipation of the spring arrivals. It takes weeks of rain and snow and sun and wind to weather the houses and rid the wood, or what have you, of human smells and the fresh paint and the pesticide taint from the store. Besides, the winter is getting long, the extra time heavy — so turn to and build a birdhouse. It's fun, easy, satisfying, and may even attract a bird family that will give you joy during the coming unfrozen months.

Fortunately, birdhouses are simply constructed from woods that are the easiest to work with and the most available. The two worst problems are knowing what sizes and shapes each bird species prefers in the way of a house, and how to make the house so it's easy to clean with a minimum of trouble. I'll try to come up with answers to these two problems as best I can. Before that, however, consider briefly the materials, the finish, the protection, and the location.

Wood is the best material, and in our area the best of the woods is fir, pine or redwood, and the average good thickness is one inch (3/4 inch, actually). Thinner woods can be used for the smaller houses. I like the houses to remain unfinished, so I prefer redwood, but if fir or pine is the choice, then a shellac, thin stain or a dark paint is fine. If the house will be exposed to the southern sun, white paint is good to reflect the heat.

The house should have a roof overhang to keep the rain out of the hole, the sides should be a little longer than the bottom to keep moisture out of the side joints and the bottom should have two or three small drilled holes for drainage. Proper hole sizes will keep unwanted species out of the house, and lining the outside of wood duck houses with metal keeps skunks and raccoons away.

The location of the house is important, not only as to height but as to exposure to storms and sun, nearness to some foliage, and accessibility for cleaning.

Now to the two real problems: House dimensions and house cleaning.

After pouring over many a table of house dimensions, I think the following is a good general average for some of the bird species and their house preferences in our area.

Bird	Floor	Inside Height	Entrance Above Floor	Entrance Diameter	Height Above Ground (feet)
Barn Swallow	6x6	6	(*)	(*)	8-12
Bluebird	5x5	8	6	1-1/2	5-10
Chickadee	4x4	8-10	6-8	1-1/8	6-15
Crested Flycatcher	6x6	8-10	6-8	2	8-20
Downy Woodpecker	4x4	9-12	6-8	1-1/4	6-20
Flicker	7x7	16-18	14-16	2-1/2	6-20
Hairy Woodpecker	6x6	12-15	9-12	1-1/2	12-20
House Wren	4x4	6-8	1-6	1-1/4	6-10
Nuthatch	4x4	8-10	6-8	1-1/4	12-20
Purple Martin	6x6	6	1	2-1/2	15-20
Red-headed Woodpecker	6x6	12-15	9-12	2	12-20
Robin	6x8	8	(*)	(*)	6-15
Screech Owl	8x8	12-15	9-12	3	10-30
Titmouse	4x4	8-10	6-8	1-1/4	6-15
Tree Swallow	5x5	6	1-5	1-1/2	10-15
Wood Duck	10x10	24	18	3	10-20

(*) 1 or more sides open

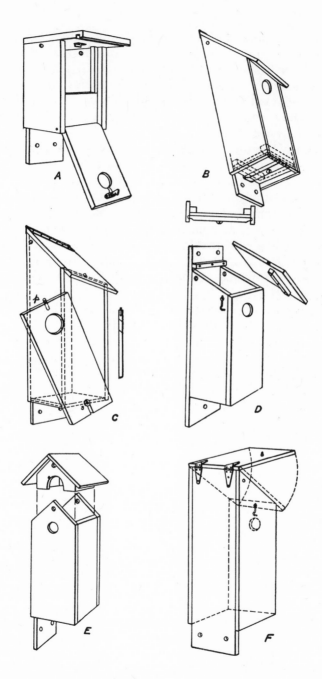

The best time to clean a birdhouse is right after a hatch has left the house. Cleanliness is important. Birds haul dirty stuff in for nests, have lice and other pests, some young die and remain in the house, and many species combine their living room with the bathroom. The illustrations of six ways to gain easy access to houses offer you a choice, depending upon the type of house.

Type A has the front hinged at the bottom and a spring catch at the top under the roof. Type B has a bottom that drops out when the cleat is turned. Type C has a peg at the top of the front that fits into a hole in the roof and a screw at the bottom that is tightened to hold the front intact. Type D has a roof held in place by side hooks and eyes. Type E has a roof that recesses into the sides and is held in place by a long dowel running under the eave. Type F has the roof hinged at the rear with the front secured by a hook and eye.

There are fine houses for sale at your local garden, hardware or farm store, and they're not too expensive. It is fun, though, to make your own house and have it occupied by a bird. No rental agents, no income to be taxed, no severe tenant problems.

That's the way to be a landlord.

March, 1971

*"...the photographer from Germany closed
his camera...and...returned to Germany...,
the picture-taking episode unknown...."*

MRS. STEWART AND THE GERMAN

I like to think it was mid-morning on a July Saturday during the 1880s that a visitor from Germany stood on the shore of Lake Minnetonka where the amusement park in Excelsior now stands. Being a traveler, he had his camera ready. Even though the wind was from the east, the sky overcast and a threat of rain was present, he still couldn't resist taking a picture of the magnificent sight of the huge paddle-boats City of St. Louis and Belle of Minnetonka racing away from the Excelsior docks. Talk about air pollution today! Smoke belched from the double stacks as the paddle wheels churned the waters, and I'll bet there was no hesitation in dumping ashes overboard when the time came.

After snapping the picture, the photographer from Germany closed his camera, hefted his bag and baggage, and sooner or later returned to Germany with the film undeveloped — the picture-taking episode unknown to lake area residents.

Years later, a person who seems to have been a member of the Lafayette Club was traveling in Germany, stopped into a photography shop for some reason or other, and lo! there was a print instantly recognized as a Minnetonka scene with tiny Gale Island in the background and the two famous boats probably beating towards the docks at the Lafayette Club. Our American traveler brought back the negative of this scene and had a large print made of it. The picture now hangs on the hall wall leading to the grand ballroom in the present Lafayette club.

Ken Kelley is a local Minnetonka historian who has always loved that picture of the Excelsior scene. Several years ago, he commissioned a Minneapolis photographer to visit the Lafayette Club and take a picture of the picture. Ken has a large print in his living room and, when I visited there a couple of years ago, he made it possible for me to obtain a small print as well as a large one of this famous scene. I plan to give my large print to the Freshwater Biological Institute when there is a wall to receive it.

In the process of carefully examining the picture, I noticed a small white sign on the south side of the wood dock in the left foreground. The sign says, "Use Mrs. Stewart's Bluing." This product is nationally known and happens to be made by a Minneapolis firm, Luther Ford & Co. Since at least ninety years have passed since that sign was on location in Excelsior, I wanted to gather the latest data on Mrs. Stewart, the product, and the company.

In the late 1800s, Al Stewart peddled his housewares from a horse-drawn wagon through Iowa and southern Minnesota (an early sale in Red Wing has been documented). One of his pet products was "Mrs. Stewart's Bluing," made from his own formula and named after his wife. The main use for the bluing was, and is, in the family wash to make white clothes whiter. The bottle label carried the picture of a very stern and serious lady who wasn't Mrs. Stewart, but rather Mr. Stewart's mother-in-law — and the passage of time has shown how the real Mrs. Stewart "blue" her chance for fame by refusing to let her husband use her face on the label.

Bluing for use in washing is made by dissolving the powder of an iron derivative, and the resulting solution is a blue liquid that makes white things whiter. There are more than 300 shades of white as determined by a spectograph or color indicator, and the whitest white is one that has some blue in it. Many soaps and detergents have blue added today, but countless numbers of women still use the original

Excelsior Bay in the 1880s

139

Mrs. Stewart's Bluing and will use nothing else.

But not only women-washers use the bluing. Over the years, lots of special uses have evolved. At Mr. Poodle, a dog beauty parlor in Miami, Mrs. Stewart's Bluing is used in the rinse water of white poodles; painters add it to white paint for really white paint; lots of people use it in fountain pens as blue ink; poultry raisers and horse ranchers swear the addition of bluing to drinking water prevents certain bird and animal diseases; many people use it as an anti-irritant for relief from bee stings and insect bites; and gray-haired ladies add it to their rinse water after shampooing to prevent an undesirable yellow tinge.

In my opinion, the most unusual use was thought of by a Rome, Georgia, man who wanted to buy the bluing in powder form. He was going to mix it with talc and a binding agent and then paint his homing pigeons' wings so they wouldn't fray during long flights.

It's fascinating how history and chances weave their spells. Little did Al Stewart realize when he placed his sign on the wood dock in Excelsior that a German photographer would immortalize it. I'll bet Al didn't plan on the bluing painting pigeon wings, either. That's a good cycle: do the wash with bluing and hang it on the line. Paint the pigeons' wings blue and let them fly over the wash. Do the wash over again using more bluing.

March, 1971

*"No bird is more gorgeous than a
male wood duck with his plumage
in high spring fashion."*

MINNETONKA'S DUCK

If an official bird is ever chosen to represent our greater Lake Minnetonka area, in my opinion it would have to be the wood duck. As in each of the past twenty-two years, one of the main joys of summer is to look forward to the arrival of the wood ducks, to watch the hatches mature, and finally to bid them good-bye well before the lake freezes over.

Many have been the evenings when we set out in the boat to see the ducks in June and July, threading our way through the Seton Channel and spotting as many as a dozen broods paddling around in the setting sun. One evening we came upon a cocktail party and a baby sitter, or so it seemed. On one side of a small bay was one female woodie and more than thirty young ones — while on the other side seven mature wood ducks were congregated as if in the living room. It so happened the water was the color of green creme de menthe also.

No bird is more gorgeous than a male wood duck with his plumage in high spring fashion. The red eyes, stylish long green "hair" lying back on his head, sharp white lines here and there, and the honey-colored lower body feathers make him a most dapper gentleman. The female is something else again. From a distance, she's on the drab side, but a close look shows her soft grays and browns with the very distinctive white circle around her eyes and a white line trailing behind the eye.

Several years ago, just before wood ducks became legal to shoot once again, I came in to shore at the end of a hunting day with my limit but with one of the ducks unknown to me. At the dock, waiting, were two game wardens and I promptly asked them what the strange duck could be. That's right, it was a female wood duck. After carefully checking my license, gun and equipment, the wardens were very understanding and left me short one duck for the day but wiser as to what a female woodie looks like.

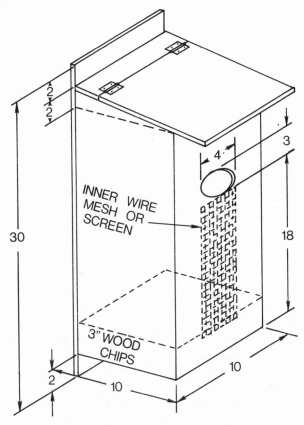

WOOD DUCK HOUSE

Male and Female Wood Ducks

Wood ducks are classed as a surface feeder duck contrasted to the so-called diving ducks. Surface ducks include the mallard, gadwall, black duck, pintail, widgeon, baldpate, shoveler, and the four kinds of teal. Their general family name is Anatinae and the official wood duck name is Aix sponsa. In Robert's *Birds of Minnesota,* he says other names for the wood duck are summer duck and carolina duck. I have never seen a woodie around before the ice leaves but, according to Roberts, some have been seen as early as March 12 and the average date of arrival is March 24. For our lake, I think it's safe to say we won't have wood ducks until there's some good open water around.

I now have five wood duck houses on my property and hope to have some tenants. Although it's a good idea to put houses up early, so they weather somewhat, it's not too late to add one or more to your trees. Good houses can be purchased (the Excelsior Farm Store has two different kinds), but a house is also easy to build. The general dimensions are 10" by 10" by 24". A 3" long hole is important because its size and shape will let a normal wood duck female in while keeping out the northern raccoons. The best woods to use for the houses are redwood or cypress one-inch boards. Hinge the top for easy cleaning, and also for taking a peek or two while the mother is nesting.

Apparently, a female will have two broods each year and lay an average of a dozen eggs. Some friends of mine, however, have seen houses with as many as twenty-two eggs in them — possibly laid by two different ducks. Sometimes the hatch is poor and only two or three eggs mature, but it seems the normal brood around Minnetonka is from seven to ten. The eggs hatch about 31 days after being laid and the babes climb out of the house within 24 hours or so after being born. Their feet have tiny sharp toe-nails for climbing and 1/4 or 1/2 inch hardware cloth on the inside of the house front serves as a ladder for them to climb. They make their way up, out, and down by themselves.

In the summer and fall, mature wood ducks love corn and acorns. I've shot wood ducks with crops full of dried acorns and they sound like rattles when shaken. Until the fall migration starts, most of the ducks at my corn feeders are woodies. I love their whistles as they fly away, low over the water with necks slowly weaving back and forth. Many years ago, another friend of mine pulled into a bay at Wawatosa Island for some early-morning bass fishing and saw the magnificent sight of more than a thousand wood ducks rise out of the morning mist and disappear like little flying ghosts.

If anybody wants full details on wood ducks, I suggest Resource Publication 60, Bureau of Sport Fisheries and Wildlife, Washington, D. C. This booklet costs thirty cents and is a compilation of information resulting from a workshop meeting of five days in 1966 attended by leading wood duck ecologists. Wood ducks love Minnetonka and I know most, if not all, Minnetonkans love wood ducks. Shouldn't Aix sponsa be our official area bird?

April, 1970

NAMES ARE FOR THE BIRDS

Among the great joys of early spring are the coming of the
summer bird residents and the passing through of the spring
migrants. According to my records and the early records
from Robert's *Birds of Minnesota,* the mass of robins arrive
late in March (which they did this year), purple martins by
mid-April, barn swallows by the third week in April, black
and white warblers and catbirds by the end of April,
Baltimore orioles early in May, and scarlet tanagers by
mid-May.

A surprising Robert's entry is that bluebirds generally
show up in mid-March, but I've found them so scarce in
recent years that I'm lucky to see one all summer long.

As much as I like birds, I'm not afraid to laugh at some
of their real names. We're accustomed to our common
birds and their names, but some real birds that we're not
used to are the Yellow-nosed albatross, the Atlantic blue-
faced booby, the skunk-head coot, the melodius grassquit,
the marbled godwit, and the mesquite boat-tailed grackle.
One of our more uncommon local birds is the tufted tit-
mouse. My wife called me at the office one morning to
announce that such a bird was at our feeder. In a very loud
voice heard by all in the office I said, "A tufted tit-WHAT?"

There's a game that can be played that involves the
names of birds — but birds hardly likely to show up at

your feeder, hop around your lawn or sing cheerily in the morning. These birds are fictitious but the basis for the made-up names are only too real.

Many years ago a very funny book called *The Indoor Birdwatcher's Manual* was published. It is full of unreal birds with English and Latin names and their calls. One such is the "Hairy-chested Backslapper," (salutans vigorans), with a cry of "Hi-ya, bub."

Several weeks ago in one of my columns, I named a few of these crazy birds but the paragraph containing them was deleted. In honor of that occasion, I dedicate a local bird to him, he who jimmied my copy and who I now call "The Aggravated Snip-out," (editorans molestis), whose cry is "cut-cut-cut."

With due apologies to the indoor manual for bird watchers, I give you the following birds that are possibly visible on the local and national scenes.

Some birds are named in recognition of Minnetonka's history. Have you ever seen a Sampson's Wroom Wrenter (hostelis excelsiorans) whose yell is "eureka! eureka!" or The Great Northern Railer (wayzatans commutus) with the call "jimhill-jimhill?" Of course, all of us have experienced The Reminiscing Old-timer (streetcar-boatans et streetcar-boatans) crying "recall-recall."

Birds of Minnetonka of a more current nature are such specimens as The Agitated Channeler (narrowans speedster) with a sound of "splish-splash-splish-splash," or the ugly Oscillatoria Shaker-upper (rubescens redflagans) broadcasting "beware-beware-beware."

Even those of you not terribly interested in birds readily recognize The Bespeckled Party-pooper (nofunans wall-floweriensis) persisting with "let's go-let's go," or the Wide-Eyed Night-Bloomer (daytimeans sleepiensis), always hollering "have another-have another." Let's be sure we don't ignore The Blonde-headed Wiggle-waggle (posteriorensis motionans) chanting "yeah-yeah-yeah."

Recalling the recent political campaigns, we had many sightings of those migrants of every four years like The Great Western Fence-straddler (politico nonentiensis) with

The Poorly-Marked Tern
(Confusionis Worsiensis Confoundidimus)
Call: Honk!
from The Indoor Birdwatcher's Manual

the call "guess so-guess so" or the newcomer Lesser Lester (campaign dudans) howling "fowl-fowl."

Every day, winter or summer, we see such regular birds as The Red-nosed Cold-catcher (sneesis allthetimeans) making noises like "kerchoo-kerchoo," The Greater Gross-Speaker (loudmouthensis partiensis) sprouting "yak-yak-yak," The Yellow-bellied Pussy-footer (nostandis issuans) who can only say "don't know-don't know," or The Long Winded Phony-bird (bigshotis noisans) hollering "me-me-me."

So, during the next few weeks, watch out for the real birds traveling through and those that will stay for a while, and take with a grain of salt those nutty kinds that seem to be with us all of the time. Maybe by putting a little of that salt on their tails we can learn to live with the least desirable of our species.

April, 1969

*"Fish of each species...react differently
to the light and temperature...which
results in different fishing seasons."*

A SEASONAL TRIGGER

I would guess that by now everybody is aware of the fact
that this is a very late spring (1972). The yearly smelt run
at Lake Superior is already two weeks later than the previous
late record, and the run may not even reach its peak this
weekend. Some of the northern lakes have ice in their bays,
and I noticed in the paper that one fisherman remarked he
was going fishing with his snowmobile, trolling in the cracks
of the ice.

Coincidental with the late spring is the fact that several
northern lakes have had their walleye season opening de-
layed, and in many other lakes the opening on schedule
produced rather poor results. The timing as to when the
fishing seasons are opened takes into account the period
when certain fish are spawning. Because there are different
fishing seasons, it follows there must be different spawning
periods for different fish. Why? What makes a walleye so
different from a bass that there's a five-week span between
openings?

So, here we go again, digging into one of nature's marvels.

There's no such thing as everything being the same and
fish are no exception. In general, however, the springtime
urge for the fish in our northern areas to lay and fertilize
eggs for the continued propagation of their species is triggered by two main factors: light and temperature. Some fish

in other parts of the world have special adaptations, depending upon their environment. Some live in waters whose temperatures vary only slightly, as in polar streams. Some fish live where there is little or no light, as in the great ocean deeps. But, these are the exceptions. The rule is that the warming of the waters and the lengthening of the day turn the fish on.

Located in the head of the fish, right at the base of their brain, is a special gland — an endocrine or secreting gland — called the pituitary gland. Humans have such a gland whose front lobe, for example, secretes a hormone called somatotropin (Greek for "body-nourishing") and is essential for our growth. In fish, one of the secretions by the pituitary is a substance that activates the ovaries of the female and the gonads of the male.

As the days get longer, more and more light enters through the skin on the fish's head and that, plus the temperature of the water, triggers the gland. Fish of each species are different and therefore react differently to the light and temperature, which results in different spawning periods which results in different fishing seasons. But, depending upon their species, when a fish's time comes and the gland is activated, the secretion causes the eggs in the female and the milt in the male to develop. When ripe, the eggs are ejected by the female and the male swims over them, spraying his milt which fertilizes the eggs.

The number of eggs laid by a female depends upon her age and size, but also on the habits of her species. We have two general kinds of egg-laying fish habits: nest builders and random spawners. Nest builders lay fewer eggs because their survival rate is higher and the young are protected by the male. Our common nest builders are the sunfish, crappie, bass, and bullhead. The random layers sort of dump their eggs around and consequently need a lot more eggs to assure the survival of at least one fish to reach the adult stage per one million eggs.

Largemouth bass are late spawners because they require water temperatures between 60 and 65 degrees. They usually spawn in shallow bays and many is the time whole

Largemouth Bass

batches of eggs and young fry are killed by sudden wind changes and temperature drops that alter the bay-water temperature below acceptable limits. A large female may have up to 25,000 eggs. The male is a good nest builder and removes small pebbles with his mouth.

Walleyes start their spawning runs when the water reaches between 38 and 44 degrees. A large female may have up to 388,000 eggs, but the average is about 50,000. The eggs are spread in streams leading into lakes or on gravel reefs in the lake itself.

The muskellunge spawns later than northern pike (who spawn right after the ice goes out) but sometimes muskie milt fertilizes northern eggs and also the other way around. The result is quite a mixture of northern and muskie coloration. The muskie spawns in a peculiar way. When ready, the male and female swim side by side as if cemented together. To spawn, they roll over on their respective sides and squirt eggs and milt at each other.

Crappies have a surprisingly wide tolerance to light and water temperatures. They don't semi-hibernate in the wintertime, as do bass, and therefore lots of them are caught through the ice. They spawn later than walleyes but can spawn from May into July. We have a gravel and rock reef to the east of the Pass, and during the next six weeks this reef will be covered with crappie nests. It's not unusual to catch fifty crappies in twenty minutes. When guarding their nests, a crappie will bite on almost anything that comes along.

It's easy to see why increasing turbidity of water can affect fish life because the murkiness cuts down on the light penetrating the water. It's easy to see how the addition of abnormally-warmed water can affect fish life as the spawning habits can be altered. It isn't easy to figure out alternatives as our waters change, however. Nature has a way of changing and so must we.

The one thing we do have to remember is that nothing is simple and that one thing leads to the next. The balance of all things is extremely delicate. We must be careful as to what we do, so we don't trigger the wrong thing at the wrong time.

March, 1972

"...their feeding is so active that a pair
can easily consume two halves of an orange
in just half a day."

SOME CALL THEM GOLDEN ROBINS

Somewhere back in the wings of the Bell Museum of Natural History at the University of Minnesota is a production line the likes of which I had never seen before — until the other day, that is. And, it's understandable that such organization is necessary when the materials to make 15,000 Baltimore oriole kits are pretty much all in one place.

Dick Barthelemy, Public Education Coordinator of the museum, had a brain storm in 1969 and thought that maybe the public would like to buy the necessary material to attract orioles to their yards.

The kits are nice. You get three pamphlets, a 3-foot length of rope, and a pad of cotton. One pamphlet is on Birds of the Minneapolis-St. Paul Region; another tells you how to Cultivate Your Garden Birds; and the third is a report on the Oriole Project with a lot of details about the Baltimore oriole. The rope is for you to shred into fibers. Then the cotton and rope fibers are placed outside for nesting material for the orioles.

It takes a lot of rope to prepare these kits. Last winter, Dick was in Mexico and brought back a 300-pound bale of sissel on the top of his Volkswagon. During the trip home, the car bounced and the weight of the bale caused his Volks roof to pop in. He kicked it back, inside out. But 300-pounds isn't nearly enough rope fibers for the kits so he has been buying rope from Stillwater Prison for 10 cents a pound. So far, he's purchased 3,000 pounds.

The oriole kit is not a survival kit. The orioles still will make out whether you buy a kit or not. What the kit will do is possibly attract the orioles to make their nest near you. The kit helps to bring the birds to the people.

These brilliant orange and black male birds and the less-gaudy females are called Baltimore orioles as their colors are the same as those on the coat of arms of Lord Baltimore. A friend of mine living in Bellgrove near Hopkins had several pair show up at his sugar-water feeder this spring a day or so before mine showed up at the Pass. I had my half-oranges hanging on nails in trees when, in close order, two red-headed woodpeckers swooped down, followed by a very bright male oriole.

For the past three years, we've had two or more pairs of Baltimore orioles flitting from treetop to treetop, arching down to our feeders and treating us to song after song composed of eight single notes. During the month of May, their feeding is so active that a pair can easily consume two halves of an orange in just half a day.

Orioles can be absent after Memorial Day for three weeks or so. Apparently this is the nesting period and the four to six brown-streaked eggs will incubate for fourteen days in the long hanging nest that looks like an old-fashioned coin purse open at the top. After feeding mostly at night at a reduced pace during this period, they join the daylight world again around the third week in June and are regular feeders until heading south about September 10.

Besides freshly-cut orange halves for attracting orioles, a wide-mouthed glass jar filled with colored sugar water is most effective. A simple solution is about a quart of water to one cup of sugar and just enough red food coloring to give the solution a fairly strong reddish tinge (colorless liquids don't seem to turn them on). Bend up a wire coat hanger into both a hook and a large enough loop to slip over the neck of the jar. Pinch the wire so it nests into the threads of the jar and hang it from the hook anyplace outdoors. Orioles also love good beef suet.

ENTRANCE

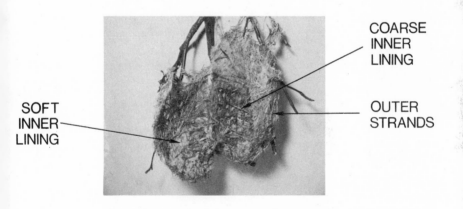

COARSE
INNER
LINING

SOFT
INNER
LINING

OUTER
STRANDS

BALTIMORE ORIOLE NEST

Recently, I was given three oriole nests to examine in detail, and a work of art they are! The nest is composed of three parts: an outer pouch, an inner cup, and fluff. The outer pouch is made of fibrous material (like the rope fibers) which weathers to a pearly-gray even though string and, in one of the nests, bits of Christmas tinsel were used. The pouches of the three nests that I had all measured 3 inches in diameter near the base of the pouch, had top openings of 2.5 inches but varied in length from 4.5 inches to 5.5 inches. The record length is 8 inches. It is this pouch hanging from tree branches and even clothes lines that gives the oriole an alternate name of "hang-nest."

Inside the pouch at the bottom is a circular cup two inches in diameter, of brown, fairly stiff long wooden fibers — like extra-long dry pine needles. A survey in 1927 found these cups to be made of long hairs from horse's tails and manes but the automobile has affected even the oriole nests and most of the long strands now come from vine strips.

Lining this inner cup is a lot of soft fluff (the cotton in the kit). Natural material used by the bird includes the pappi or silky stuff of the dandelion seed or the cottony covering of the willow seed. The eggs are laid on this soft material and you can just imagine the babies snuggling amongst the fluff. One of the three nests contained two mummified babies, their bony eye sockets protruding high over their skulls (3/8" on one, 1/4" on the other). Another of the nests was a rarity: perfectly constructed but absolutely unused — another tragedy, no doubt.

We love to have the orioles with us, but time flies, along with the birds. After the young leave the nest, the orioles will stay around for about two months and then leave in early September. They migrate south and start arriving in Central America in mid-September. They spend the winters throughout Guatemala to the Isthmus of Panama.

Dr. Louis Daniel, an old friend of mine, must have had the oriole in mind when he wrote a poem entitled, "Here Today — and Guatemala."

April, 1972

"...reproduction is accompanied by changes to the senses...odors, colors, actions, light and temperature...."

BECOMING A MAMMAL MAMA

Why is springtime the time when "a young man's fancy turns to love?"

Why do so many species bear their young only in the spring?

Why do the ducks along with the other birds and the bees show the greatest sexual activity in the spring?

Nature has the evolutionary answer; food is the most plentiful and at its best in the spring. It takes a bit of planning to accomplish springtime births. Take the deer. It has a gestation period (from fertilization to birth) that averages 201 days, and the fawn is born in the spring. How do the deer know to give this birth leadtime of 201 days?

Again, nature has it planned. Backing up to September or so of the previous year, the male and female come into "rut" and "heat" at the same time. Fertilization can take place and the egg develops into a beautiful fawn by April or so of the next spring. Over eons of time, those deer that did not have sexual periods in the fall for spring births had their offspring die off. The strain didn't continue. Survival of the fittest once again.

To me, the months of March, April and May are the best of the year. Not only is it great to observe the seasonal change from winter to glorious spring and enjoy the arrivals from the south, but the wonder of birth and rebirth on all sides is a never-ending show more dazzling, beautiful and complex than any ever staged by man.

As I write this, I glance out a window past the bird feeder to the lakeshore a few feet away; the dapper-red cardinal is again busily tending his lady-love by offering bits of saffron seed while she demurely sits deep under the spreading boughs of a red cedar tree. Not long ago in terms of minutes, this season's first three-bird flight of mallards came by, one drake chasing a drake-hen pair that apparently dared to consider a potential nesting spot in the first drake's established territory.

The cottonwoods, the lilacs, the birches and maples have buds fairly ready to burst, so fat that when looking at the sky up through the branches, it seems as if the leaves are already out. Open waters along the shores are warmed during the day by the sun, attracting those fish that are triggered by the rising water temperatures. And, what do you know, also by the open waters are the fishermen, not wasting a day in pursuing the fish even though ice still covers the waters not ten feet from shore.

The miracle of reproduction is accompanied by changes to the senses that make the propagation of the species a possible thing. Odors, colors, actions, light and temperature that change come springtime, plus permanent things like men's facial hair, lions' manes and the antlers on deer, combine to give spring the center of the stage for the mating game.

All living things have molecules arranged into cells that can reproduce. This reproduction is done in two ways: by mitosis or simple dividing of the cell into two identical cells; or by meiosis, which is a complex halving of the cells into cells which are truly only halves instead of two whole cells as in mitosis. Humans and most mammals have their cells divide by meiosis, although a rare happening does come along when mitosis in man occurs and identical twins are the result.

Man's body cells have sets or pairs of things called chromosomes. The chromosomes in sex cells have pairs of genes or hereditary molecules, with the number of pairs varying

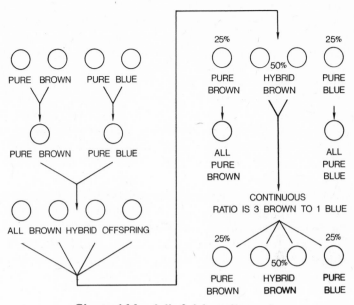

Chart of Mendel's 3:1 heredity ratio

with the species, such as man. The real miracle molecule is a thing called DNA which is what makes a man a man, a robin a robin, or a walleye a walleye. "DNA" is short for a nucleic acid in our genes. The long name is deoxyribonucleic acid. First proposed as a theory in 1941 and proven in 1952 as the base of heredity, DNA, in the book *The Double Helix* makes fascinating reading. The complexity of reproduction and DNA is such that more than six billion steps are involved in the formation of a normal man. When a sex cell divides in man, it is split into half egg and half sperm, each with only one-half of the genes and DNA of the original cell. When these cells are joined with others in fertilization, a new and distinct thing is created. The combinations are almost limitless because man has over 40,000 genes. The fertilized egg may become a new human that is similar to the parents but never identical. Twins can be identical, yes, but never can the child and a parent be identical.

Gregor Mendel defined the law of heredity, and the

familiar three-to-one ratio is still a constant. The color of eyes is used as a standard example of how it works. A man with pure brown-eye genes and a woman with pure blue-eye genes will have children with brown eyes, no matter how many children. Brown is dominant over blue and the new sex cells from the parents are made up of half brown and half blue genes, so brown is always the children's eye color. But the children have both brown and blue-eye genes, so their children express the Mendelian law of three-to-one. Their children will have three offspring with brown eyes and one with blue eyes (a cell with brown and blue genes mixing with one also with brown and blue genes results in a new cell with two brown-eye genes, a second cell with one blue and one brown gene, a third cell with one brown and one blue gene, and a fourth cell with all blue genes; the result: three brown eyes and one blue, since brown is dominant over blue.)

As an egg develops into a certain species (because of DNA) with its own characteristics (because of genes), its growth into a delivered offspring varies. In mammals, a few species like the duckbill platypus lay eggs and the offspring feeds on the egg until hatching. Some mammals deliver their young from the womb while still extremely immature (like the great kangaroo whose baby weighs one ounce and is ½ inch long at birth, following a forty-day gestation period). Their offspring actually swim through the mother's fur after birth to reach a pouch where they crawl in and hang onto a food nipple for weeks and months as they mature. In most mammals, like man, offspring stay in the mother's womb until "maturity," getting their food through the placenta (Greek for "flat cake") and are born fully developed.

It won't be long before we start seeing the results of this spring's miracle of birth. The muskrats are on the prowl, the cardinals have been whistling, the owls have been hooting and the rebirth of plants with their tender shoots and succulent bark will provide that needed food for those that depend upon it for growth.

Springtime is here. To what is *your* fancy turning?

March, 1973

160

"...what you and I are today we owe to all of those people of the past. They gave us today and the very least we can do is give others tomorrow."

SOME SIDES TO MEMORIAL DAY

I belong to the generation whose grandfathers and grandmothers are long dead; whose mothers and fathers, with their friends, have had their ranks badly depleted; and whose friends are facing a time when their ranks will start to thin rapidly. In short, my generation is the middle-aged generation with the meter running.

Memorial Day should be a day of memories and respect for those who have died. All of us probably do pay respect to the dead to a greater or lesser degree. But the degree of respect, however, is generally limited to those whom we knew as close relatives and friends.

In my opinion, all of us should give utmost respect to nearly every person who has ever lived. I say "nearly" everyone because there have been a few, I'm sure, who were such that memories of them are best left alone. But what we are today and what we have today — for better or for worse, depending upon how you as an individual wish to look at it — we owe to those who were here before us.

Think what we owe to the philosophers and their concepts of law and order and justice and politics. Think what we owe to the medical profession, and the miracle drugs and operations and pain killers and transplants. Think what we owe to the scientists and our industry, and lunar modules and high-flying jets. And think what we owe to those whose foresight saved our lake from total commercialism around its shores, built the dams and bridges, established some zoning and all in all made it possible for you and for me to fish and boat and swim and totally enjoy one of the greatest freshwater lakes in the world.

These are the people for whom we should hold our Memorial Days. These and our relatives and friends whose lives touched us, whose heartaches and failures saved *us* from some, and from whose victories we continue to reap the rewards. Those of us who think we're such hot stuff should stop and think what our lives would be like without electricity, radios, automobiles, synthetic yarns — and yes, sewage plants. What would we do suddenly thrust upon a moon-like surface with nothing, placed in a situation where we had no past to rely upon and therefore hardly any future to look forward to. No culture, no books, no music, and no meaningful life.

So, my point is that what you and I are today we owe to all of those people of the past. They gave us today and the very least we can do is give others tomorrow. There are all sorts of ways we can pass things on: through an honest society, more knowledge through higher education, active participation in politics, doing our best with the job at hand, whether at home or at work.

In the regular concept, Memorial Day was first observed May 30, 1868, and was so ordered by General John A. Logan, commander of the Grand Army of the Republic. Its prime purpose has been to honor the dead of all of our wars but only part of our country does this. Eight states in the south observe what is called "Confederate Memorial Day" June 3, which is the birthdate of Jefferson Davis, who became the first president of the Confederate States of America in February, 1862.

Two odd pieces of information. WWI and WWII had the Germans as our enemies, among others. When you walk into Arlington National Cemetery, the countless rows of white crosses are everywhere, but the very first white marker is that for a fallen soldier named Bromley H. German. Secondly, I have been told that the first soldier killed in WWI was from Evansville, Indiana, a German named James Bethel Greshan.

On a recent trip in May to Washington, I was between the airport and my hotel when I impulsively directed the cab to go to Arlington National Cemetery. Ten days ahead of time, I observed Memorial Day standing by the low circular limestone slab with the flame flickering in the middle that marked the resting spot of a fallen commander-in-chief. It has remained a relatively simple place with green grass containing three flat black rectangular stones lying near the eternal flame.

The left one reads, "Patrick Bouvier Kennedy, August 7-August 9, 1963."

The middle one says, "John Fitzgerald Kennedy, 1917-1963."

The right one only has, "Daughter, August 23, 1956."

My initial visit to this gravesite was in 1963 and it was an emotional thing. The news of President John Kennedy's assassination had reached me just as I was walking across Piccadilly Circus in London early in the evening. If possible, all of Europe was shocked and grieving just as much and, in some cases, even more than Americans. It's human nature to want to be home at time of disaster and I returned the next day.

A very few weeks later, I was standing by the still-fresh dirt of the President's burial site, observing the thousands of people filing by — all deeply touched by the many hats lying on the grave, each representing a branch of the service headed by this commander-in-chief.

One woman threw her bracelet onto the grave, to land among dozens of other items strewn about. I asked a guard about this and he said so many people tossed valuables onto the grave it was necessary to clean off the site each night and haul boxes of things worth thousands of dollars for safe keeping in the Smithsonian Institute.

Today, thousands visit the grave each day as well as Robert Kennedy's gravesite 100 feet away. An interesting point is that only one out of fifty people visiting Arlington now go to the Tomb of the Unknown Soldier. Perhaps that ratio is more in the favor of the Unknown Soldier on Memorial Day, at least.

May, 1969
May, 1971

Part 3

THE SUMMER SEASON
June through August

*"The adult firefly crawls out during the mid-part
of June with the sole purpose of propagating
the species. They don't even seem to eat."*

WHEN YOU'RE HOT, YOU'RE HOT

During most of our warm and calm June evenings, just as
dusk is giving up to darkness, the air over the marshes and
tall grass fields is dotted with the love flashes of the firefly.
The best display that we have usually seen occurs as we glide
by boat through the Seton Channel at closed throttle in mid-
June. The cackling of the blackbirds has been stilled for the
day and the young wood ducks tucked away by their mother.
The performance of a lightning bug night takes center stage.

I've always loved to see the fireflies flitting here and there,
and one of my favorite remembrances as a kid was the night
I trapped several fireflies in a quart Mason jar, took the jar
to my room, and fell asleep to the gentle pulsing glow of the
special soft "fire."

The blinking light that you see appearing here and there
on a June night is the male of the firefly species sending his
own distinct signal to the female who is perching somewhere
on the tip of some slender reed or long grass. These fireflies
are really beetles and have spent up to two years in the worm
stage. Suddenly, the larvae go into a metamorphosis by
building sort of a case around themselves. The adult firefly
crawls out during the mid-part of June with the sole purpose
of propagating the species. They don't even seem to eat.

These "lightning bugs," when in the adult stage, spend
their limited number of days in the marshes and tall grass,

but as dusk falls, they crawl to the end of branches or weeds, shoot a few test glows to get sort of warmed up, and then the male takes off to fly. He sends his own form of a Morse code which only the female of his species can recognize. She answers in her own way which only he can recognize, and he lands near her for mating. The female lays her eggs in a few days, they hatch in a few weeks, and the larvae become our "glow worms" and stay that way for one to two years.

There are forty species of fireflies in North America, but the most common one (such as ours) sends a flash of about ½-second duration every five to seven seconds. In so doing, he makes a kind of "J" pattern in the air by dipping slightly when starting to flash and then rising rapidly towards the end of the flash. If you're out in the marsh and want to find a female firefly yourself, take a small penlight and flash it very quickly every six seconds or so. She'll answer, even if you don't make the "J" pattern. If you want to act like a female, wait for a male to blink, then flash the penlight about every two seconds with a flash duration of about one second. As the male gets closer, lower the penlight towards the ground because the actual female diminishes her glow as the male gets closer.

Every species has its femme fatale. One popular North American species, photuris, can imitate the flash of other females of other species. She attracts the males, which she promptly eats.

People have always been fascinated with fireflies. They are common in ancient Japanese art and even popular music recognizes their life cycle, like Johnny Mercer's "Glow little glow worm, glimmer, glimmer. Turn on the A-C and the D-C." The Chinese wrote about fireflies 3,000 years ago.

The light given off is totally efficient. In other words, it's all light and no heat, compared to our common lightbulb with is 10 percent light and 90 percent heat. The intensity of the light is small, about one-400th candlepower, but some species can brighten up to one-50th candlepower. The firefly can control the making of the light at will. It contains a chemical called "luciferin" which is activated by another

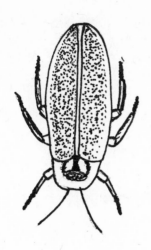

TOP VIEW   UNDERSIDE

FIREFLY

chemical called "luciferase." With oxygen present, a nervous impulse produces the luciferin which glows in contact with luciferase.

The firefly has few enemies because it tastes terrible, but there is a species of tropical frogs which dote on fireflies. In season, one will eat so many that the glow from the bugs inside make him look like an X-ray negative.

The fanciest glow worm is a South American fellow called the railroad worm. It has eleven glow-spots along its sides much like portholes in a ship's side, plus a red glowing head-lamp. In Thailand, there is a species that lights up together every 120 seconds and the simultaneous light is enough to bathe an entire river in an eerie light.

So, when you see a firefly firing away over the cattails

and by the reeds, feel for the poor guy. His life is doomed to a few hours or days. But then, with the kind of mission in life that he has, I suppose there are worse ways to go.

June, 1972

A MYRIAD OF PYRAMIDS

There are several kinds of pyramids. The best known are the Mexican and Egyptian stone monuments of a pyramidal shape with square bases and triangular sides. Of these many pyramids (75 in Egypt alone), the granddaddy is the Great Pyramid located just outside of Cairo, Egypt. It is immense. Its base would cover eight football fields (more than 13 acres); its present height is 451 feet; its top is flat, 36 feet on the side; and the whole structure is composed of 2,300,000 limestone blocks, each weighing 2 ½ tons. That's some pyramid! — but only one type.

Another type is the mathematical form from which other "pyramids" get their names. It is a solid with a polygonal or several-sided base and whose sides are triangles and meet at a point at the top of the pyramid. By this description, a mathematical pyramid can have a number of different sides, but the common pyramid has four sides. A cone can be regarded as a pyramid with a round base.

Our lakes have their own form of a pyramid, but one which is not necessarily three-dimensional and can be drawn as a two-dimensional figure forming a triangle. This pyramid can be called a "life's" pyramid because it represents the relationships within the food chain of one species to another. The base of the pyramid is for the lowest order of the food involved and the highest form of food is the tip.

171

Most living matter must depend upon feeding on other matter for food. Plants are an exception, however, because they make their own food through the magic process of photosynthesis. Because of this ability to make nutritious food from water and carbon dioxide, triggered by sunlight, plants form the base of most of life's pyramids, even our own.

Most Minnesota lakes are well known for their excellent bass fishing, and for a good reason; conditions necessary for an adequate bass-life pyramid are ideal. Plants (algae) form the pyramidal base. Although some algae are consumed directly by fish, the vast majority are eaten by minute water animals (zooplankton) and other "neither fish nor fowl" organisms in the water. They, in turn, are gobbled up by small fish — "minnows" in the general sense — and bass eat the minnows. The pyramid is complete, simply and directly.

An added dimension to the pyramid must be considered, however. When a one-pound bass is caught and placed on the stringer, in effect the stringer must be a strong one because that bass represents 2,700 pounds of algae and water animals hanging alongside your boat. To have good bass fishing in a lake, a lot of algae and a lot of minnows are required.

But 2,700 pounds of plankton for a one-pound bass? That's a pile of plants and animals and an explanation is certainly in order.

Proper fish and game management has proved that to harvest one bass from a lake, two bass must not be caught so the species will continue to propagate. For each minnow that each of these three bass eat, two minnows must not be eaten. For each algae and little water animal eaten by each of the minnows, two must not be eaten. Also, it has been demonstrated that for a pound of minnows to grow to that weight, 10 pounds of algae are needed — and a pound of bass needs 10 pounds of minnows. The result of all this is a pyramid drawing which shows that a one-pound bass that is caught and two that are not caught need the food support of 90 pounds of minnows (30 pounds eaten and 60 pounds uneaten) and the minnows need the food

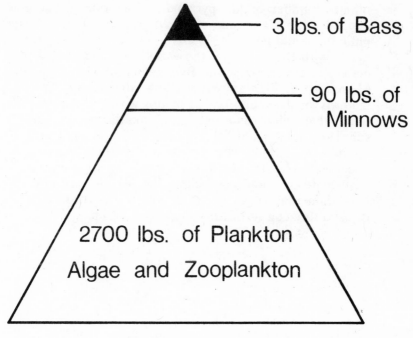

Life pyramid of a bass

support of 2700 pounds of plankton (900 pounds eaten and 1800 pounds uneaten).

A lake without algae and zooplankton is a lake without fish. Experiments have shown that "old" lakes near residential areas, heavily populated and used, support up to fifteen times the number of fish that "new" lakes do that are sparsely settled and unpolluted by chemicals. If you're a fisherman, some algae in the water is a good thing. The problem before the House of Lakes, Rivers and Streams is to get back to a balanced amount of algae, depending upon the use to which we wish to put any certain body of water. The number of pounds of fish per acre in a lake like Minnetonka is astounding. A somewhat reduced number of fish through a reduction in the algae would never be noticed and our water would be clearer, better, and most inviting.

This life pyramid of a bass is just one example of the

infinite number of life pyramids. Take ours. Man must depend upon plants and photosynthesis for food. A simplified pyramid for us is "Plants - to meat - to Man". Intermixed with this are all of the varieties of the animal, vegetable, and mineral needs. But, plants are the things that MAKE food. Plants are the things that supply the vast majority of available oxygen in the world. Plants are the things that unlock and make available the minerals of the soil. Hurray for plants!

There are countless angles to these life pyramids, but one point is clear: nothing can really exist by itself. We have to realize, and appreciate, the interdependency that is fundamental to all life. Man must never forget that he is just a tiny cog in this big, big wheel of life.

June, 1968

*"Every organism is literally plugged into
its environment....tied into terrestrial
space-time to a fantastic extent."*

BIOLOGICAL CLOCKS

Last Saturday evening we were fishing for crappies over the reef to the east of the Pass. There was a light southeast chop to the water and the boat kept swinging gently as it pivoted around the anchor line. In between moderate action on our lines, we discussed the reasons behind the varying activities of fish as to feeding times, locations and other habits.

We talked of the solunar tables, which are based upon the combined effects of the sun and the moon, and gradually the conversation reached that of the biological clock. All of us had traveled extensively and all of us have our own way of combating the change of times during long travels.

It is common knowledge that international airline pilots must follow fairly specific schedules of their own that they have developed from experience to help live with the constant time changes. I know that the pattern I have developed when going to Europe works for me. I take a morning plane east, arrive and go to bed early in the morning of the new time zone. Then, I get up at noon or so and enjoy the rest of the day before getting a full night's sleep that evening.

From almost his very first day, man has been aware of the changes in the moon and the sun, the stars and the planets, and over the thousands of years has built up a lore and a science that has changed with the cultures and the gathering of more and more scientific knowledge. Today, the search continues as to just what things are affecting all of us, and how. It all relates to our biological clocks.

For instance, an extensive experiment is underway, using what is called a SAMI or Socially Acceptable Monitoring Instrument. This is a British development that consists of a six-channel recorder about the size of a transistor radio that is worn by people involved in the test. It is worn 24 hours a day, and every minute over a 30-hour period a measurement is taken and recorded on the strip chart. Blood pressure, pulse, temperature, posture, respiration, and other body variables are charted and the variations noted.

From these readings, and countless other experiments and tests, a lot of very fascinating things have come to light. It has been found that the moods of a person swing and change about three to four days before coming down with a common cold. There is a marked change in a person's blood pressure over a 24-hour period. One doctor constantly took his own blood pressure over an extended period and found that his highest pressure of the 24-hour period occurred exactly at 2:30 P.M. every day. He noted that all of his physical examinations had been given him in the morning and a peak blood pressure had never been noticed.

Other experiments have shown that cell division rises and falls over a 24-hour period, that the rate of hatching of moth eggs does likewise, and that the secretion of the cortical hormone in rats ebbs and flows over an approximate 24-hour period.

In general, there are two broad biological clocks, and within each clock are two schools of thought.

One clock, the approximate 24-hour clock called the Circadian rhythm or clock, was defined by a University of Minnesota professor. The other clock, called the Circannual rhythm or clock, operates on a yearly basis. Within these two are the advocates of the theory that influences on the clocks are caused by internal forces, and the other faction claims the influences are all external. Most evidence shows a perplexing mixture of reactions by people — almost

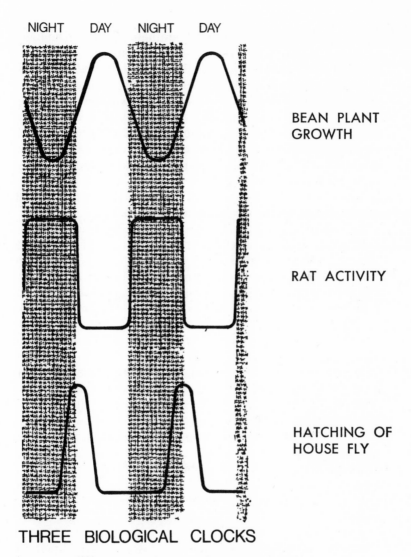

NIGHT   DAY   NIGHT   DAY

BEAN PLANT
GROWTH

RAT ACTIVITY

HATCHING OF
HOUSE FLY

THREE BIOLOGICAL CLOCKS

as many different patterns as there are people.

There are "night people" and there are "day people." The former seem to function best at night and are slow starters in the morning. One thing that has been found is that these types don't experience a rise in their body temperatures until about ten in the morning.

An extended experiment with animals has shown that by forcing an animal to constantly adjust to changes in its biological clock, the effort of doing so shortens its life by as much as 6 percent. Another experiment showed that on one day a controlled kill of living matter with amphetamine was 78 percent effective, but yet was only 8 percent effective another day under seemingly exact conditions.

One thing is for sure. Whatever the forces, external or internal, and whatever their origins, they are affecting every living thing from man on down. They involve our living habits, our moods, our physical and mental well-being, and extend into spheres of influence such as bird migration. It has been documented that the sand flea Talitrus navigates during the day by "shooting" the sun and then is able to "shoot" the moon at night, also. While doing so, it can correct for the passage of the moon as it crosses the heavens. As one scientist has said, "In this tiny flea apparently is built a remarkable instrument — a solar-day, lunar-day clock compass."

A Professor Brown is a leader in the "external forces" camp and feels that the clocks are measuring the rhythms of the environment. Rats sealed in a box run three times as much when the moon is below the horizon as when above.

Dr. Brown says, "Every organism is literally plugged into its environment. If you see an animal, concealed from all obvious information, telling you the phase of the moon, the time of the year, the condition of the tide and the precise time of the day, I think it's time to admit that it's getting considerable input from its environment." And he goes on to say, "I am beginning to believe more and more that organisms are tied into terrestrial space-time to a fantastic extent."

What an interesting world; what a fascinating complex of forces. Little do we really know just why the crappies act the way they do when they do, but we can find out some day. It's going to take a long time, though.

June, 1972

SHOOTING FORTH THE FIREWORKS

The greatest fireworks display I've ever seen was shot off a little more than 48 hours after the Minnetonka area tornadoes of Thursday evening, May 6, 1965. We were in Tivoli Gardens, Copenhagen, Denmark, trying to cheer ourselves up after being informed by cable that our lake home had been destroyed by the twister.

Tivoli is one of the entertainment wonders of the world and that certain Saturday evening it rained cats and dogs (or whatever it rains in Denmark), the outdoor play at the Peacock Theater was cancelled, and rides and shows were soaked. But then, there's always a consolation. At about 11 P.M., the skies cleared, the moon shone brightly on the glistening benches, and thousands of colored lights sparkled and reflected on and through millions of hanging raindrops everywhere. And the fireworks went off on schedule. To this day, its amazing to me how the garden management could put on such a display of pyrotechnics night after night, year after year. There's only one word for it — tremendous!

Our usual viewing of fireworks is during the evening of the 4th of July at the Lafayette Club on Minnetonka's Crystal Bay — from the broad northern lawn in the early years, by boat for the past many years. The sum total of anticipation, travel, fireworks, boats, horns, whistles, chants, cheers, and the ohs and ahs surely surpass any and all other fireworks experiences anyplace, including Tivoli.

I had an interesting session with the Arrowhead Fireworks Co., Inc., in St. Louis Park, the suppliers of the fireworks to be shot off at this year's celebration at Lafayette. Their warehouse is crammed with shells (don't call them bombs), and various wooden frameworks with fuses running all around. I readily agreed with the big sign that announced in no uncertain terms, "No Smoking."

Nearly 300 different kinds of shells and ground displays are stocked in the St. Louis Park warehouse for Fourths of July, county fairs, town centennials, and official doings of all sorts throughout the year. I can just imagine an important board of directors' meeting at a fireworks manufacturing plant, faced with the tough decision as to what to name some of their new shells and ground displays. Can't you see them finally agreeing on current names for shells such as Golden Veil, Flitting Butterfly, Wiggling Serpent, Clinging Vine, Diamond Jewel, and Weeping Willow? Or ground display titles such as Elephant Washing Her Baby, Devils at Play, Tree of Paradise, Fish-eating Pelican, and Firemen to the Rescue? These and other shells and displays are listed in a catalog that also contains flag displays with only 48 stars in all of the pictures. Maybe something more than fireworks should be fired.

This same catalog offers these firing instructions, among others: "Anyone handling fireworks should be cool-headed and careful"; "If a shell fails to leave the mortar, never reach in to pull it out (you may lose an arm)"; "If you have a shell that failed to explode in the air, find this dud shell at all cost." It's obvious that major pieces of fireworks are dangerous and only competent hands should work with them.

I had never seen a fireworks shell close-up. Its construction is simple, of course. A mortar — a piece of large diameter iron pipe — is buried two-thirds of its length in the ground (about two feet), slightly angled into the wind if there's a wind. The cylindrical shell with a long fuse is dropped into the mortar, the fuse is lit, and all hands stand back! Trained men do the firing and their work is so planned that ohs and bangs fill the spans between bursts.

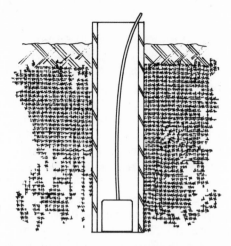

CROSS SECTION OF FIREWORKS
AERIAL BOMB

Have you ever wondered what makes the different colors in fireworks? I did, couldn't get a local answer, and finally talked with the Star Fireworks Manufacturing Co. in Danville, Illinois. Chemicals are the color answers. The "reds" come from burning nitrates and chlorates of strontium, the "greens" are generally nitrates of barium, and the "blues" are usually copper sulfates like those contained in the old-time garden poison, Paris green. The white spray-stuff is nothing but powdered aluminum in various sizes of bits, depending upon the desired effect. Salute shells are a highly-concentrated aluminum powder that fires all at one time. A regular four-inch aerial shell (costing as little as $1.60 each) contains about two ounces of a high-in-the-air bursting charge of saltpeter and charcoal with about a half-pound of star powder to make the color and spray.

This year's program at the Lafayette will be comprised of 141 shells, fired individually and set off just fast enough so that the whole shebang will be smoke and dust inside of 15 to 20 minutes (paid for by Lafayette Club members on a volunteer basis).

The fireworks program includes simple one- and two-break shells of various colors (names weren't specified), nine-inch

Salutes (the "touchdown bombs" at Gopher football games), and imported shells with names like "One-Ring and One-Chain," "Colored Peonies," and "Changing Flowers." This year's big shell is a hot seller called "Jackie Gleason," patterned after the spraying burst of fireworks seen each time on the Jackie Gleason Show. I don't know just where in the Lafayette program this shell will be fired, but I do know that the one shell costs $15 and is 15 inches in diameter (I suppose in relation to the real Jackie Gleason in both girth and cost).

Watching the display is great fun. All hands try to guess what the color of the next shell will be as each one is fired. "Red!" "No, green!" "No, white!" The all-out favorite of us kids is what we call "Popcorn." Any and all shells are great with their concussion on firing, their slightly fuzzy trail as they arch the 350 to 450 feet into the air and then pop, hiss and spray their colors that die all too quickly. But, "Popcorn" is something else again. The official name is "36-shot Finale" — a big central explosion of pure white and then a grand display of lesser explosions much like white Jolly-Time popping like mad.

Although the making and firing of fireworks is a dangerous business, it must be satisfying to develop a new design, give it a good name, have its sequence go off in proper order, and to hear the shouts and murmurs of pleasure and praise as the colored fire graces the sky.

Fireworks on the glorious Fourth of July have always been a welcome spectacle against the beautiful backdrop and surroundings of Marvelous Minnetonka and I'm sure this year will not be an exception.

June, 1968

Note: This evening of fireworks at Lafayette Club was spectacular, all right. The "Jackie Gleason" misfired at the start of the program, arched 20 feet into the air, and then fell back into the supply of shells. The entire display went up in a grand explosion. Nobody was hurt but the program was shorter than usual! — like all at once.

182

*"...each morning is the beginning
of the end of your life...."*

NEW GLORY EVERY DAY

The Fourth of July and Old Glory go together and rightly so. Perhaps this Fourth has special significance for our flag because of the anti-war and the anti-this, anti-that and even anti-flag that has been happening. One of our physical laws is that every action has an opposite and equal reaction, like pushing backwards in a canoe and the canoe goes the other way. Some portion of this law is being shown by the reactions of many by displaying more flags on flagpoles, stickers on cars, emblems on uniforms, and pins in lapels.

During my recent business trip to Europe, I wore an American flag-pin in my lapel and was proud to do so. After business in seven countries and attendance at the Swiss Industries, Milan, Paris, and Hanover, Germany fairs, the conclusion that I reached is that America is admired, respected and regarded as the world's leader. But not all people think this. One person admired my flag-pin and stated he had always felt the British were the best. I didn't point out to him that he apparently had his flags mixed up.

I happen to believe in our country, not necessarily "our country, right or wrong," but rather loving it in spite of its faults. Nothing is perfect and to expect something to be so is an error, in my opinion. Because something does have some faults doesn't make it all bad. Even beautiful flowers have imperfections.

It was back in 1814 when Francis Scott Key wrote the Star Spangled Banner after seeing Old Glory still flying over Fort McHenry. This flag is still in the Smithsonian Institute but it isn't like our flags of today. This old one has 13 stars, 8 red and 7 white stripes, and measures 30 by 40 feet. It also has a mysterious red "V" in one of the white stripes. In 1818, the present pattern of 13 stripes and a star for each state was adopted.

Old Glory on the Fourth is just fine, but for me each new day brings new glories, bathed in patriotic reds, whites and blues. A while back, somebody made the remark that each morning is the beginning of the end of your life and you better make the most of it.

Take the reds of the day. The gorgeous sunrises and sunsets with pink and purple clouds and shafts of sun rays fanning up and away; the brilliant spring plumage of the proud male cardinal; the hotness of the setting sun on the reflective stripes of lake buoys and in the shiny windows of the houses along the eastern shores; the sunburn on tender faces, backs and arms, accenting the watch strap on the wrist and the bathing suit strap on the shoulder; the pupil of the wood duck eye, set like a ruby in a ring; the rump of a catbird, the throat of the butter and eggs weed along the shore, the head crests of our downy, hairy and pileated woodpeckers, my red cabbage in the garden — and even the red chromate paint of the Enchanted Island Bridge.

Take the whites of the day. Fleecy good-weather clouds lazing along, usually moving west to east from altitudes of 5,000 to 35,000 feet or so, shifting in their forms to create fanciful figures if you're so inclined; sparkling water in the whiteshafts of a full moon in the dead of night; the natty breast of the nuthatch; a squirming grub worm objecting to the sudden exposure during hoeing; the brand-newness of three tennis balls fresh from the can following the hiss of the pressure release and the smell of rubber; a cauliflower head unwrapped from its protective leaves, fully formed and ready to cook; Minnesota towheads in the summer sun; newly-painted dock sections with their paint mixed with

The whites of clouds at the start of a new day

some sand to offset slipperyness — and even the distinctive wide eye-ring of the female wood duck.

Take the blues of the day. A cloudless sky of unmatchable blue and a clear dark night sky sprinkled with stars; the coarse wing quills of a five-week old mallard; young blue jays laboring in their efforts to learn to fly; the delicate bluebells nodding in the gentle breeze; the two dripping blooms of my Vanda orchid plant from India; those Scandinavian eyes so common around here; the perfect color shade of the bloom of an egg plant, so subtle and fragile and beautiful; the heavenly-blue-flame of a wood fire; the belted kingfisher perched on a limb looking the lake over.

One evening near the shore of a part of the lower lake, I met a fresh independent spirit, and, to be so fresh this spirit had to be young. She was. Six years old, four upper front teeth missing, a volatile thing whose green eyes snapped with an interest and innocence that made me want to cry.

Here we were, she and I, surrounded by people, a soft night with warm light, the birds flitting and the grass green — and this elf of a female with the little warm fanny on my lap really cared that she liked her Hershey bars without nuts while I preferred the ones with almonds. Every so often, she would slip down off my knees to dash over the lawn into a weed patch to pick fresh clover blossoms for the two of us to suck, she sticking her blossom-end in her mouth while I conventionally chewed the stem-end.

For her, life is a going thing. She wants to know everything, she wants to look at everything, she wants to feel and listen and really be a part of whatever there is. It's hard to imagine anything dampening a lively spirit like this one.

If we could only rekindle this kind of spirit in everybody — the young spirit concerned with nuts in Hersheys and new good things that can be done. If the fresh independent spirit could become universal again, then we could really celebrate the Fourth of July as a continuing day of American independence and our colorful flag would fly high, wide, and handsome in the eyes of everyone — again.

July, 1970

"...the hostess for the party...showed me a letter
I wrote to her husband following the party.
I had forgotten about...it...."

A 1953 LETTER IN JULY

In 1953, Robert A. Taft died, William Holden was named the best actor for "Stalag 17," "From Here to Eternity" was the best picture, Audrey Hepburn was best actress in "Roman Holiday," Miss America Neva Jane Langley had green eyes, General George Marshall won the Nobel Prize for Peace, and Winston Churchill won the Nobel Prize for Literature.

But that wasn't all. The annual Fourth of July picnic of "our group" was held at the base of Brackett's Point on Browns Bay, Lake Minnetonka. This gathering had met since World War II and has always been a lot of fun with all of the kids, babysitters, dogs, games, and suppers.

It has been eighteen years since 1953 (this is written in 1971) and our Fourth of July group still gets together. This year the location is on Smithtown Bay, and the crowd gets larger with new additions. Since 1953 we have lost two.

It was quite a crowd, even in 1953, and, just the other day, the hostess for the party on that Fourth of July eighteen years ago showed me a letter I wrote to her husband following the party. I had forgotten about the letter but it does document the occasion. Here it is:

July 10, 1953

Dear Harry:

It is an established fact that there were several people

at your house on July Fourth, and it also was most apparent that a goodly number of them were children. In the Quest for any child, however, the Wright one was usually found.

Many important occasions are being documented and preserved by our Government for posterity's sake, and I think the gathering at your house on Independence Day (by that is meant independence of our Country, obviously not of the parents) should be factually presented as a worthy candidate for inclusion in the Time Capsule along with atomic bomb films, Wayside Garden's Catalog, Truman's sport shirt, and the rise and fall and rise and fall and rise of America's own Kaiser.

To be factual, it is necessary to establish conditions to properly evaluate the attendance. To begin with, there are four stages of attendance:

STAGES OF ATTENDANCE
1. Actually present
2. Possibly present (this is explained later)
3. Should have been present
4. Could have been present

In the following Table of Values, proper credit, in the opinion of the judges, is being given to the classification of attendance types:

TABLE OF VALUES

Adult Man	1 Point
Adult Woman	1 Point
Adult Woman (pregnant)	1 ½ Points
Child - Boy	1 Point
Child - Girl	1 Point

Taking the four stages of attendance, the points as listed in the Table of Values were applied in the following manner: Stage 1, full credit; Stage 2, ½ credit; Stage 3, ¼ credit; and Stage 4, no credit. With these facts in mind, the attendance was tabulated as follows:

STAGE 1:

Adults	38 ½ Points
Children	47 Points
Total	85 ½ Points

STAGE 2:

Adults	1 3/4 Points
Children	1 Point
Total	2 3/4 Points

(NOTE: This stage includes the Glueks and two children observed walking near your house, and assumes the possible pregnancy of Mrs. Quest, Mrs. Wright, and one other woman unknown except Mrs. Gray who is included out but definitely.)

STAGE 3:

Adults	1 3/8 Points
Children	3 1/4 Points
Total	4 5/8 Points

(NOTE: This stage includes McCaffreys, Reeves, and Mrs. Winter plus their children, all or in part, plus children of parents present that were absent plus pregnancy of Mrs. Reeves.)

STAGE 4:

Adults - Zero Points but possibilities unlimited.

Children - Zero Points but possibilities unlimited.

(NOTE: This stage contains a multitude of factors and therefore people. A few examples of this attendance stage would be Mr. Atwood's former wife and children; Dr. Rizer's former wife; Mr. Hensel's former wife and children; Mrs. Rizer's former husband; my Aunt Lydia from LaCrosse, Wisconsin, whose son is Mr. Wizard on television; my sister's aunt by marriage who complained one time that her daughter's baby of three months wouldn't eat radishes; and President Eisenhower if you had sent him an invitation as there were many present and future voters at hand.)

A recapitulation of these point totals based upon the Table of Values and the Four Stages of Attendance shows an actual attendance of 85 ½ points and a potential attendance of 93 1/8 points.

You are to be congratulated on a well-run affair — one that must be enjoyed from year to year as evidenced by the attendance.

Yours for bigger July Fourths,

Dick Gray

*"Lake Minnetonka's origin stems from the sand
and gravel from melting glaciers deposited
around huge blocks of ice — land-locked
icebergs, so to speak...."*

A SECOND-CLASS DIMICTIC

Several years ago, a friend of mine in Switzerland said very casually to me that he had an acquaintance in Chicago and, being from Minneapolis, I must know him. I replied that although I knew lots of people, the 415 miles separating the two cities plus the combined population of several million made it somewhat unlikely that I would know his friend.

I tell this story to illustrate the fact that everything is relative. To my Swiss friend, Chicago and Minneapolis are next to each other and the dots on the map that represent the two cities are awfully small.

So it is when speaking of Lake Minnetonka — this "relative" business, I mean. During the past weeks, many people have told me they have never seen the water in Minnetonka so clear. They were saying this even when the water by the Pass was still full of the severe red bloom of Oscillatoria rubescens.

The Pass water is now clear and I, too, must say that the lake is abnormally clean — so clear in fact that when I went out to find my diving raft anchor last weekend, I not only found the usual one but I also found one I lost several years ago.

What's "relative" about all this? Simply that Lake Minnetonka is really many lakes in one, and no general statement about lake conditions — except for lake level, maybe — can be accepted as the gospel truth for everyplace. It's pretty general knowledge that the upper lake and the lower lake are different, but I agree with the Conservation Department when it states that Minnetonka is made up of three kinds of lakes: the prairie-type lake of western Minnesota (the fertile western and northern upper lake bays), the hardwood lake of central Minnesota (the open areas of the upper lake), and the coniferous or pine lake of northern Minnesota (the usual waters of the lower lake).

Lake Minnetonka's origin stems from the sand and gravel from melting glaciers deposited around huge blocks of ice — land-locked icebergs so to speak — thousands of years ago. The differences in the three lake types is a chemical one, resulting from different soils, land configuration, and use by man — mainly from the land configuration and the way the land has been used surrounding the bays, channels, and open reaches since the lake was born.

Just imagine the various different pressures brought to bear on the lake as a whole by wind, weather, and man. The islands, bays, and channels all react differently to waves than do the deeper open reaches of water. Natural conditions vary from year to year — more or less rain and snow, few or many thunderstorms (and an occasional tornado!), and warmer or cooler summers resulting in severe or mild use of the lake by man.

But then, factors vary from season to season and from one day to the next. Certainly hot summers and cold winters are the seasonal extremes, but other major things that you may not think of affect the lake. Activity in the water varies widely from nighttime to daytime; sunny days cause more photosynthesis than do dark cloudy days; and calm water compared to rough water has its effects on water turbidity and temperatures.

The results of these different factors on different parts of the lake which have different chemical make-ups become graphically clear when certain facts and figures are considered. The occurrence of certain fish varies widely; walleye fishing in the lower lake is far superior to the upper lake and bullheads are common in Halsteds Bay but rare in the main upper lake. Types of algae found can be so different from one bay to the next that the samples could be from lakes separated by thousands of miles (witness the red algae bloom in the main upper lake but not in either the lower lake or the fertile western and northern bays of the upper lake.)

The chemistry of the distinctly different bodies of Minnetonka water is widely variable. For instance, total phosphorous concentrated in surface water samples taken by Robert Megard on June 27, 1968, (expressed in micrograms per liter) was 217 in Halsteds Bay, 120 in Harrisons Bay, 45 in Crystal Bay, 39 in the main upper lake, 108 in West Arm, and 66 in Browns Bay. In general, phosphorous concentrations decreased during the summer, but in some areas they increased.

Minnetonka is regarded as a temperate second-class dimictic lake, but that's not bad, that's good. The fancy words and classification tell a limnologist, one who studies lakes, the general character of a lake.

Lakes are classified by two general ways: their location in the world and their general water depth.

1. Tropical lakes — where the water stays at pretty much the same temperature the year around and there is no circulation or overturn of the water from wide temperature changes during the season.

2. Subtropical lakes — where one circulation or overturn occurs each year; cooler winter temperatures cause a water temperature drop but the water never freezes.

3. Temperate lakes — where the lake overturns twice a year (which makes them dimictic) generally about six months apart and the surface freezes part of the year (this is Minnetonka's class).

4. Subpolar lakes — where the lake is dimictic with two overturns but one is for a short period during a brief summer.

5. Polar lakes — where the water is frozen all or almost all of the year and perhaps one overturn may occur during the very short time of thaw.

Lakes are grouped by depths into:

A. First Class — lakes so deep that the lake bottom never gets warmer than 39.2 degrees F. (the temperature at which water is heaviest and therefore stays on the bottom).

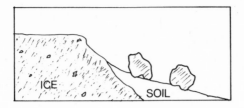

ICE
BLOCKS
DROPPED

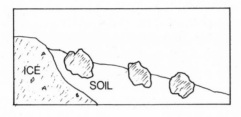

ICE
BLOCKS
BURIED

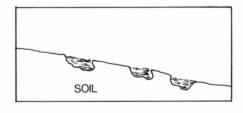

ICE
BLOCKS
MELTED

THE BIRTH OF ICE-BLOCK LAKES

B. Second Class — lakes, like Minnetonka, of moderate depths where some bottom warming occurs to help in mixing or overturning the water.

C. Third Class — lakes so shallow or warm that the water is all the same temperature.

Minnetonka, being the kind of lake it is, has a special water temperature balance during the spring, summer and fall months, and that area in the lake where this balance occurs is called the thermocline.

It happens this way: as the sun melts the ice and warms the surface water, and as the winds and currents mix the water, the colder water goes beneath the warmer water because cold water is heavier than warm water during these months. Sooner or later, the sun, wind and waves can't reach deep enough to mix the water so a band of rapidly changing water temperatures is established. The cooler water remains at rest, below this band called the thermocline. In Minnetonka last weekend, the thermocline was at a depth of about seventeen feet, was about eight inches thick and in these eight inches the water temperature changed from 72 degrees to 59 degrees. Perhaps this thermocline band was this narrow because we had a series of very warm days, moderate nights, and almost no wind to upset any balance.

Strangely enough (to me, at least), lake temperatures weren't studied until 1820 when some of the lakes in the Swiss Alps were examined. With the use of the thermistor-type of thermometer (since 1953), rapid and precise temperatures can be taken. I use a special electrical set-up made up of a thermistor which we put together at my office; it works like a charm, measuring instant changes by the ability of the thermistor to conduct an electrical current as its temperature changes.

Technically, thermoclines are defined as regions in lakes where rapid decreases in temperatures occur. The Germans call the region of change the "sprungschict" (sounds awful, doesn't it?), and the English call it the "discontinuity layer." People with chalk and blackboard define it as:

$$\frac{\theta=d^2 \ \theta=0}{d_z^2}$$

but don't try to figure it out. You can't get there from here.

We don't need a formula to know that our Minnetonka water warms up, cools off, freezes, thaws. But down below, don't forget, there is that layer of balance so vital to the fish, weeds and algae. The thermocline is our friend, as is that second-class dimictic body of water — Marvelous Minnetonka.

July, 1968

"...two growth rings are added, a lighter...
'spring ring' and a...darker 'summer ring'."

GROWTH RINGS

I was walking towards my vegetable garden Sunday, following the usual path, when I suddenly realized the route was nearly grown over by a bush. A closer look at this particular shrub made it clear that some of its branches had shot out more than a foot this year. If the same amount of growth occurred next year, my way to the garden would be completely blocked.

Lilac bushes planted three years ago have new shoots fifteen inches long. A red cedar near the house shows growth of only two or three inches. The silver cedar on our deck has hardly an inch of growth. A beautiful and big flowering crab by our front door proudly waves seventeen inches of reddish new growth in the western breeze.

I'm making two points. One, most of the growth of woody plants occurs in the spring and summer seasons; and two, each plant and tree has its own rate of growth. It therefore follows that the conditions for growth during a season, when applied to any particular species of woody plant, can be determined if the plants or trees have a way of recording the growth. They do, in their internal growth rings.

The three main parts of a woody plant are the crown, the trunk, and the roots. From inside out, the central trunk is made up of the heartwood (inner old wood, usually darker than the other wood), the sapwood which carries the sap upwards, the cambium layer which is the source of new sapwood and new bark, the inner bark layer which carries liquids to the cambium layer, and the outer bark that serves to protect the tree.

Each year, the cambium layer builds new sapwood. In the process, this added layer of wood around the tree makes a distinct ring of new growth. Each year, there are usually two growth rings added, a lighter and larger "spring ring" and a smaller and usually darker "summer ring". By carefully analyzing the number of rings and the condition of the rings, the age and history of a tree can be accurately laid out.

A relatively new scientific discipline has sprung up to study tree rings, because if the rings can be properly analyzed, the environmental history of the area of the tree can be told. This new discipline is called dendrochronology, "dendron" being Greek for "tree" and the rest of the big word implying time. This new study is further broken down into dendroclimatology to study past climates, dendroecology pertaining to past environmental factors, and dendrohydrology which investigates past water and runoff conditions. So far, tree rings have helped to trace conditions back as far as 8,000 years ago.

You might think that to check the growth rings of a tree, it is necessary to cut down the tree. Not at all. A very simple tool is used that is little more than a hollow drill. A boring into the tree is made and a core of the boring accumulates in the hollow part of the drill. It is removed and analyzed. Before any particular tree is used to investigate the past, so-called cross-drillings are made. This means that a series of cores are taken from surrounding trees and their growth rings checked against each other to be sure there is a general pattern. Usually about 50 years of growth is cross-checked.

All sorts of things affect the rate of tree growth and must be taken into consideration when analyzing the rings. Young trees grow faster than old trees. Young trees grow slower when very young and shaded by larger trees, but then make a big spurt when their crowns top out and they are the masters of the forest.

More precipitation gives more growth, and therefore

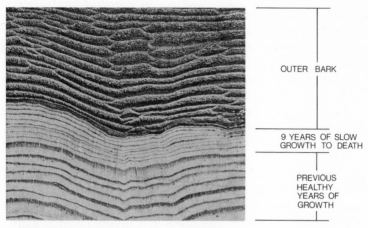

OUTER BARK

9 YEARS OF SLOW
GROWTH TO DEATH

PREVIOUS
HEALTHY
YEARS OF
GROWTH

THE DEATH BY SMOG OF A JEFFREY
PINE TREE AT LOS ANGELES, CALIFORNIA

rainfall amounts relate directly to growth rings — although in some trees, dryness one year causes less growth the next year. Certainly temperature is a factor, not only during the growth season, but at other times like winter when especially severe weather can severely retard the advent of spring growth.

Some trees are more affected by the seasonal climate than by conditions during growth. The pinon pine is most affected by winter while the bristle cone pine is most affected by the summer climate of the previous year. Variations in topography, elevation, special local conditions, and even atmospheric pressure can affect the growth rings, and therefore the rings give a key to the past for these things. This is important when you realize that the oldest tree in California is 4,600 years old and that wood from archaeological sites in the Southwest have supplied a chronology going back to 273 B.C.

My friend, Hib Hill, examined a section of a 3½ foot diameter burr oak which fell on his property near Christmas Lake in 1962. There were 229 growth bands around a hard core and he was able to determine that the tree was a seedling when George Washington was born, was 125 years old when Minnesota became a state, and experienced something that caused a drastic slowing down in growth around 1790. Throughout the life of this tree, the temperatures, rainfall, ground water levels, and conditions of the surrounding forest had their effects on the growth rings.

Now, along comes man, adding a new dimension to tree rings. Growth of the trees is being affected by our environment and what we're doing to it. As you can see from the picture, a Jeffrey pine in a forest near Los Angeles shows that just under the rough dark bark layer, there have been nine years of severely retarded growth of new wood — caused by smog and the reduction of sunlight and addition of pollutants in the air. The tree was finally cut down after its leaves failed to develop after the ninth year, but the tree rings clearly showed its troubles years before there was any external evidence of damage.

Are you interested in dendrochronology? Some foolish person has said there is nothing new anymore, that all there is to learn has been learned. Oh boy, we're just beginning and the opportunities for study are absolutely unlimited. A fascinating pursuit would be to pursue the science of growth rings. There is a riddle to solve in every tree.

June, 1972

*"Our waters have been changing in quality
...we have an affluence of effluents."*

A GAME OF NAMES

At this time of year families of birds and animals are still together. The offspring are growing up but are not old enough to fend totally for themselves. During this period, groups of one thing or another are seen, and that doesn't happen regularly during the rest of the year.

The other day, a friend of mine saw three young red foxes playing in the middle of the road near Howards Point. She had a fine look at them as they all but ignored her, finally slipping away into the ditch. I had several immature gray squirrels chewing away at my oranges set out on trees for the orioles. Ten mallards of an early hatch visit my neighbor's feeding spot daily and one of them is starting to show some male coloration, and early the other morning there were several cedar waxwings in our large red cedar, the older males flashing their yellow underparts and the young still wearing their striped plumage.

This group activity made me wonder what these families and groups are called, and I remembered reading an article in the *Natural History* magazine which dealt with special names for such groups or families of animals, fish and birds. It seems that after the turn of the century, Sir Arthur Conan Doyle of Sherlock Holmes fame wrote a story called "Sir Nigel" and part of Sir Nigel's training to be a nobleman was to know the correct terminology for families and groups.

I can partly equal Sir Nigel's training by saying my friend saw a skulk of foxes, my neighbor has a paddling of ducks, and there was a dray of squirrels at the oranges.

We're all familiar with a school of fish, a flock of sheep, a herd of elephants, a litter of pups, a swarm of bees, and a slate of candidates. Since they are not of a local vintage, not many of us would be familiar with a pride of lions, a gam of whales, a pod of seals, a mustering of storks, or a building of rooks.

For the farmer, however, there's a rafter of turkeys, a murder of crows, a plague of locusts, a pace of asses, a peep of chickens, a drift of hogs, a sounder of swine, a drove of cattle, and a trip of goats.

For the sportsman, there's a covey of partridge, a sloth of bears, a walk of snipe, a nest of rabbits, a fall of wood-cocks, a dule of doves, a bouquet of pheasants, a gang of elk, and a spring of teal.

For the birdwatcher, there's a pitying of turtledoves, a gaggle of geese (on water) or a skein of geese (in flight), a watch of nightingales, a tidings of magpies, an exaltation of larks, and an ostentation of peacocks.

For the fun of it, I've dreamed up and collected some family and group names that were not at all familiar to either Sir Nigel or Sir Arthur.

A chore that must be done after a hard rainstorm brings to mind what terminology should apply to the several boats that collected the water: we have a bail of boats.

Associated with these boats are the docks projecting out from the shoreline: we have a dickery of docks.

Near the docks, dotting the waters nearby for use by the swimmers, are the numerous floating rafts: we have a raft of rafts.

Hanging around under the rafts and docks are swarms of fish, liking the seclusion and the shade afforded: we have a moon of sunfish.

Clusters of sailboats gathered together before and after the races project their masts skyward: we have a forest of sailboats.

Our waters have been changing in quality over the years

A Skulk of Foxes

because of the increase in various effluents flowing into them: we have an affluence of effluents.

Updating our life's progress and the increase in quality (?) of living, we have a trip of hippies — or a smash of cars — or a jam of traffic — or a quiver of cowards.

In the current biological sense, Florida has a croc of alligators, zoos have a squirm of snakes, Australia has a pocket of kangaroos, Spain has a ring of bulls, and certain bird lovers have a mess of canaries.

Saluting our space successes, we have a capsule of astronauts. Geographically, we have a drawl of Texans. Physically, we have a wrench of bad backs. Medically, we have a blotch of measles and patients with a threshhold of pains. Hennepin Avenue on a Saturday night has its plot of detectives and a spirit of drinkers.

I almost got religion when somebody suggested that all of those people in the Basilica were a mass of Catholics.

My favorite of all of these dreamed-up groups is one that

I proposed, which possibly explains the favoritism. I have frequented many a locker room and, therefore, have seen group after group that can be labeled a charley of horses.
How does that grab you?

July, 1969

GETTING TO THE BOTTOM
OF THINGS

While in Switzerland recently, I had another of my favorite talks with a philosopher-scientist friend who is a devout follower of Rudolph Stiener. Somehow we were discussing the possibility of man having extra senses which are available to him but not used because he doesn't know he has them. My friend told the story that is supposed to be true of the blind man walking along a pitch-black street. He suddenly turned to his left and went through a small opening in a brick wall. The blind man explained that he can tell where things are by a form of "feeling," a sense that he had developed because of his blindness.

And why not? It's not inconceivable that we have a built-in sort of radar system much like a bat who can fly through an intricate series of wires in the dark and not touch anything. He emits high-pitched squeaks and the sound-echo tells him of objects ahead.

The principle of using radio waves to identify an object came into full flower during World War II in the form of radar, which means "Radio Detection and Ranging." Radio waves travel at the speed of light or 186,000 miles per second (it takes 2.4 seconds for such waves to travel to the moon and back). By using a signal source that turns off and on, and therefore emits bursts or pulses of waves, rotating antennas can be used to scan an area by sending intermittent signals and receiving the echos or bounce-backs during the sending pauses. Radio waves rebound so accurately when hitting an object that the form of the object, like a ship or an airplane, can be determined, and its exact distance from the radar set can be computed from the elapsed time. One micro-second of time equals 164 yards in distance.

Another form of the radar principle is sonar, short for Sound Navigation and Range. Sonar uses sound waves rather than radio waves and is used essentially for underwater detection. Sound travels slowly, only 1,100 feet per second, and I suppose the bat technically uses sonar. Before radar, ships sailing the north seas would spot icebergs in a fog by calling ahead and if the voice bounced back, the distance and direction of the iceberg that the voice hit could be calculated.

I spent some time last Friday afternoon witnessing a convincing demonstration of some new sonar equipment soon to be placed on the market within the price-range of all boaters and fishermen. We were on a pontoon boat out of Paul's Landing on Browns Bay, loaded with people and equipment, on our way to Crystal Bay and a check of one of the deepest parts of Lake Minnetonka. A very expensive recording sonar unit was in operation and used as a positive check as to the workings of the other much less expensive units. As we approached the buoys near the Arcola Bridge, the continuous-strip recording of the depths made it very clear why it's prudent for all boaters to observe the buoys. There's danger inside the buoy areas.

As we entered Crystal Bay beneath the Arcola Bridge and rounded the point, a sighting was made on the Noerenberg Bridge into Maxwell Bay, and we made a run at idling speed across Crystal Bay to the north of Grassy Reef which is north-northeast of the Lafayette Club. I put together the accompanying strip from the recorder to show several of the fascinating things that were picked up over several runs back and forth in the same approximate area.

The strip clearly shows the cross-section of that part of the lake with the exact profile of the bottom. The dark band along the water surface is caused by interference from boat

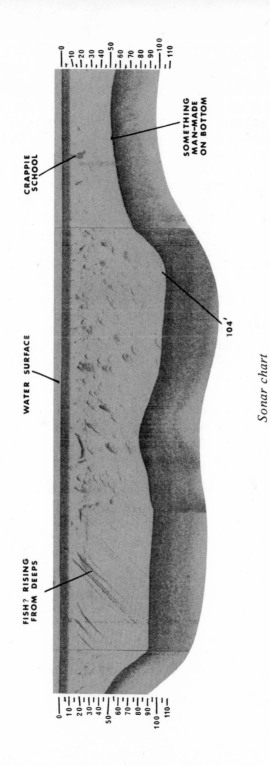

Sonar chart

205

action, weeds, algae, and general commotion. Note the number of dark spots in the center of the strip. These are fish and one of the men aboard, who has fished this area for years, could hardly wait until he could rush home for his fishing equipment and return with his spoon plugs to troll fairly fast at a depth of 25 feet. Most of these large fish were probably northerns, judging from the crescent-shaped path they made (fish even make distinctive patterns by their swimming actions).

A great mystery is the slanting lines of something excited by the sonar waves, rising fast from the 100-foot depths to within 12 to 15 feet of the boat. Monsters in Minnetonka? This coming weekend I'm going back to this spot to take deep water samples to check for oxygen. If there is no dissolved oxygen in the deep water samples, then there can be no fish. If not fish, then what?

Sonar is a great scientific tool and will soon become an everyday tool for the average fisherman. A local Minneapolis company will be placing the "Fish-Scout" on the market, a complete sonar unit selling for less than $70. I predict a large market for this, and I hope they get it. They've developed a fine product, and they're a bunch of nice guys, too.

July, 1970

Note: A week after writing this column, I made a check of a deepwater sample taken at the 100-foot depth spot. The temperature was 47½ degrees, the hardness 10 grains per gallon, there was a pH of 7.7, and there was no dissolved oxygen present.

"A 500,000 KW 'nuke' or nuclear fission power plant uses about 425,000 gallons of cooling water per minute."

WE'RE IN HOT WATER

During the one or two weeks before and after the first of August our lakes' waters will be at their maximum temperatures for the year, probably around 80 degrees. It is impossible to state exactly when the peak temperature is reached because of the many varying factors. Calm days with a hot sun produce above-normal surface temperatures. Parts of the lake that mix thoroughly with each mild wind will have a higher average temperature through the depths than those areas that don't mix readily. But, one thing is for sure: because of our geographic area of living, we accept as normal the annual heating of our waters, the growth of certain weeds, the blooms of certain algae, and the change in fishing patterns that occur as the waters warm up or cool down.

What has been and is hard to accept is the heating of our waters by man's unnatural acts of adding heated liquids to our rivers, streams, ground waters, and lakes. Whatever criticism is leveled at industry must be shared by all of us. The problems must be understood by all of us and the eventual balance that will be found must be arrived at by all of us.

The electric power industry has been the usual whipping boy for the heating of our waters, but we should keep in mind that certain Ohio waterways with concentrations of heavy industry have water temperatures as high as 105 degrees. But the fact does remain that as a general statement, 80 percent of all water used for cooling is used by the power companies. The demand for more power today produces a direct demand for more cooling water. You, me, all of us, are the creators of this basic demand for more power and we are the basic recipients of the problems that can and do result.

The electric power needs in our country have doubled every ten years since the end of World War II. The Federal Power Commission estimates that demands on the electric industry will require two thousand additional plants the size of the Monticello, Minnesota, plant (roughly 500,000 kilowatts) by the year 1990. This means that on the average, one hundred of these plants per year or about two every week for the next twenty years must be placed into operation.

Whether a power plant is energized by the use of coal, oil, or nuclear fission or fusion, the principle of making electricity is essentially the same. Water is heated to make high-pressure steam and this steam is used to turn a turbine which turns a generator that makes the electricity. Cool water must be used to condense the used steam back into water and, in the process, the cool water is itself heated somewhat by the heat exchanged by or absorbed from the steam. Immense quantities of cool waters are used in this process.

A 500,000 KW "nuke" or nuclear fission power plant uses about 425,000 gallons of cooling water *per minute*. I multiplied out the millions and billions of gallons of water needed per day and per week just for the new plants over the next twenty years and the figures became too large to be meaningful. But, these figures do focus on the fact that demands on our water supplies are real, are serious, and must be met somehow as long as you and I keep demanding more and more power.

Many suggestions and experiments have been made to utilize the warmed discharge waters from power plants, whether from fossil fuel plants or nukes. Some suggestions are to use the water to heat buildings, melt snow on highways

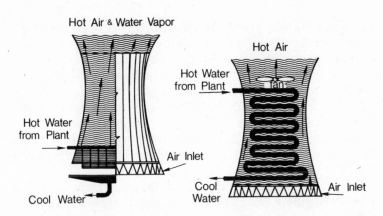

Hot Air & Water Vapor

Hot Air

Hot Water from Plant

Hot Water from Plant

Air Inlet

Cool Water

Cool Water

Air Inlet

"WET" COOLING TOWER   "DRY" COOLING TOWER

and airport runways, and produce a new industry in fish farming. But, it's not a simple thing. The discharge waters aren't really hot but rather average from 90 to 100 degrees. Extracting the heat is very inefficient because of the tremendous volumes of water that pour from a power plant, plus the fact that so many of the suggested uses are seasonal. If the waters are to be used constructively, the use must take the water minute by minute, day by day, year by year.

Nobody is more aware of the warm-water discharge problems than the electric power industry and I'm sure that in the years to come, a most familiar sight across our country will be the cooling tower. Rather than dump the warm waters into our lakes and rivers or into holding ponds, the best answer seems to lie in these towers. As the two diagrams show, there are two basic types: the "wet" cooling tower which emits hot air and water vapor out the top, and the more expensive "dry" tower which re-circulates the water in a closed system and only the air is warmed up and emitted from the top. No American company has built one of the latter type yet (1971).

The controversy over thermal pollution by the power industry continues, but we shouldn't forget the fundamental thing is that the problems have been caused by all of us and the effects of these problems aren't understood by any of us. I like the recent statement made by my friend, Dr. Donald Mount, who is director of the National Water Quality Laboratory at Duluth. "Any temperature exerts an influence, and the expected results of heat addition will vary with the season, species, latitude, altitude and the chemical and physical characteristics of the water;...disagreement...is the result of our failure to comprehend the truly extreme complexities of the interactions affected by a temperature change."

And, also "well said" is the statement made some time ago by NSP (Northern States Power) officials in reply to criticism: "After all, we live here, too." They have children and grandchildren; they hunt and fish and breathe; they live here too, and are trying to do the reasonable thing to solve their problems — caused by us, which also includes them.

July, 1971

*"It was a beautiful night for grandpa
and grandson to be together."*

DANNY SPENDS THE NIGHT

With his overnight bag all packed sans toothbrush, Danny
was ready when I came to pick him up late Saturday afternoon to spend the night at the lake. After the appropriate
good-byes that didn't take too long, we climbed into my
Ford wagon and as we drove out his driveway, he com-
mented on the fact that we both had on our striped pants.
His were more colorful, with oranges and blacks, while
mine were muted blues and natural stripes.

On the way, I asked him where he'd like to eat and he
said he really didn't care, just as long as he didn't have to
eat tomatoes or onions.

It was a beautiful night for grandpa and grandson to be
together. The air was fresh, the lake calm, the grass in full
health with that rich green of late spring and early summer
growth. Dan is all baseball right now and had brought his
mitt along. We dug out a hardball from the basement
baseball box, fully autographed with inked names that we
couldn't read but quite possibly went back to the old
Nicollet Park days, and played catch for an hour. For a guy
not quite seven, Danny is a fine ball player. He fields nicely
with proper stance and mitt in position, and out of nearly
a hundred very high balls thrown to him, he dropped only
one. He's pitcher on his neighborhood T-ball team and grins
when he says he's hit three home runs so far this year.

We decided to go to the Lafayette Club by boat for supper because Dan had never done this. On the way, he wanted to amble around Wawatosa Island where his family beaches their houseboat for overnights, and then we picked up some minnows at Kehoe's for crappie fishing on our way home after eating.

The big red numeral 35 on his long-sleeved shirt stood out a little in the grill at Lafayette, but his steak didn't last long after it arrived. Danny is a good conversationalist and we chatted merrily. His favorite Twin is Cesar Tovar. Why? Answered like a true baseballer, "Because he gets lots of singles and doubles." Strangely enough, he couldn't think of the name of a single football player who was a hero. Hockey is something else. Bobby Orr is Number 1, Phil Espirito Number 2, and the Gumper the odds-on favorite on the North Stars. I don't think Danny was aware of the fact that he ate all of the french-fried onion rings.

Fishing in late evening was slow and only two sunfish were caught, which was OK as it was getting late and dusk was arriving. He helped me button up the house for the night, checking the greenhouse dove for food and water, and then we both fell asleep while watching the East-West football game on television. We had made the agreement that the last one asleep turned off the set. I guess I did.

The bacon was sizzling along when Dan walked into the kitchen for breakfast. He had on his "morning clothes," shorts, a green long-visored baseball hat, and a green short-sleeved shirt with a small number 3 on front and "Yankees" on the back. His shoes were off, as usual, and the maroon socks were askew. He wouldn't touch his orange juice until all of the food was in front of him, and only then proceeded down the line with juice, eggs, bacon, and milk.

With the top down and the morning sun warm in the cool air, we took off in my inboard to check the water around the lake. Dan could read the thermistor thermometer meter and even at his young age was amazed at the sharp temperature levels within the lake. We took three complete readings to cover the three general types of chemical lakes that make up Minnetonka's complex — at the Pass on the Upper Lake,

Danny and friend

Lafayette Bay on the Lower Lake, and Halsteds Bay —
and at one spot in Lafayette Bay, there was a 13-degree
difference in water temperature between 22 feet and 29 feet.

At the Pass, the water was 46 degrees at 29 feet, compared
to 50 degrees at 35 feet in Lafayette Bay, and 65 degrees at
23 feet in Halsteds Bay. All three places had about 70-

degree water at 12 to 14 feet and surface temperatures varied from 72½ to 74 degrees. Lafayette's secchi disk reading was 5½ feet, at the Pass four feet, and Halsteds was three feet. The usual early summer bloom is underway and University of Minnesota graduate students at work on Halsteds claim the bloom has been doubling daily during the past week or two. Their samples are carefully analyzed in the Freshwater Biological Institute's mobile unit on location at the water patrol headquarters.

Danny wanted to take some crappies home with him so we caught three and then cleaned them, along with the two sunfish from the night before. The sunnies were both females crammed with roe, and the three crappies were males full of milt. Dan has always been interested in severed fish heads and has no qualms about squishing the yellow-orange roe between his fingers and pondering over a crappie heart as he fondles it, feeling the resilience of the red organ. Maybe he'll be a doctor some day, or a taxidermist.

On the way back to his own home he was quiet, which is usually the way at the end of an experience. He was slouched in the car seat, dangling the baggie with the cleaned fish in front of him, and finally announced he preferred the golden skin of the sunfish to the black and white of the crappie.

Driving back to my own home alone, I was quiet, too. The freshness of a young mind and spirit is a wonderful thing. It's too bad kids have to grow up and away from the charm of youth. I only wish more of them would never lose it.

June, 1972

*"...at any given instant, there is an average
of 1,800 thunderstorms in progress."*

THUNDERSTORMS

To my younger golden retriever, Molly, a thunderstorm is
a nerve-racking experience. Since the 1965 tornado, which
she rode out while our house was destroyed, Molly can tell
of the possibility of a storm hours in advance of its arrival.
She begins by hanging at our heels wherever we go, starts
to pant like mad as time passes, then gets positively frantic
even before I can hear or see signs of a storm — and she's
infallible. We now keep a supply of tranquilizer pills on hand
which she takes obediently.

To man in general, thunderstorms are an essential part
of the process that brings us our major rainfall. They occur
all of the time, even in winter, but in our area they are most
common during the summer when days are hot and humid.
Worldwide, they occur most often between the latitudes of
30 degrees north and 30 degrees south — and at any given
instant, there is an average of 1,800 thunderstorms in
progress. Molly doesn't know how lucky she really is that
she is subjected to only about 50 to 60 days a year during
which we have thunderstorms (that's still an average of one
day a week).

My most dramatic view of thunderstorms was a couple
of years ago when I took off in a French Caravelle from the
Stockholm airport. The area was full of pulsing, boiling
thunderheads, and for a half hour we pranced around and

215

between them. It was an awesome sight but amazingly smooth flying.

A thunderstorm is an everyday thing, and therefore you'd think that full knowledge of and about them would be old hat. Not so. It was not until after World War II that a group of daring pilots volunteered to intentionally fly into and through thunderstorms to probe for answers. This started a long series of flights with subsequent analysis so that by today, the science of the study of storms is very advanced — aided greatly through the use of the weather satellites, high-speed cameras (up to 25,000 frames per second), and computers.

There are two types of thunderstorms: local (more or less individual thunderheads), and severe (with broad squall-lines). Last Saturday night we had local thunderstorms (remember how hot and humid it was during the day?), and Monday morning a good squall-line came through during the night and Molly and I counted five distinct storms that hit us at the Pass over a period of three hours.

Simply stated, thunderstorms start by warm, humid air rising to form the familiar cumulus (for accumulation) clouds. The hotter and more humid the air, the higher will be the top of the cloud. Huge billowing thunderheads are common to us late in the afternoon, and these top out at around 25,000 feet. I've flown around thunderheads over 50,000 feet high with violent updrafts inside.

As this hot moist air rises, it starts to cool (at the exact rate of 5.5 degrees F. per 1,000 feet) and the moisture starts to form rain drops using impurities in the atmosphere as nuclei for the drops. Also, as the air cools, energy is released through the process of cooling and mostly negative charges build up in the cloud. Sooner or later, we get rain from the condensed moist air, lightning from the energy released, and thunder from the noise created by the lightning heat (45,000 degrees F.) violently expanding the air around it.

Severe squall-lines occur when a broad cold front meets warm moist air, forcing the warmer air upwards, and the result is a king-sized mass of thunderheads and thunderstorms. This situation also breeds tornados and explains why

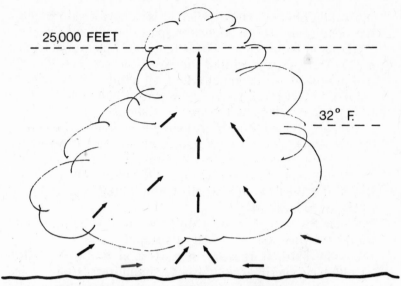

25,000 FEET

32° F.

FORMATION OF A SINGLE THUNDERHEAD

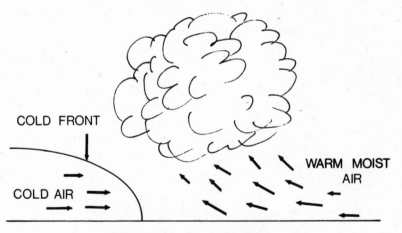

COLD FRONT

COLD AIR

WARM MOIST AIR

FORMATION OF A SQUALL LINE

217

the weather bureau knows when to issue a "tornado watch"; the conditions are just right for spawning violent weather. Updrafts in large thunderheads have been measured as fast as 200 feet per second and the air at the extreme tip of a massive head has been checked at minus 70 degrees F. A lot of energy is released when warm air is suddenly cooled from plus 100 degrees F. to minus 70 degrees F.

Because thunderstorms are part of our daily life, and so is dog Molly, I'm trying to figure out a way to "leverage" her fear of storms. Perhaps she could be rented out to Joe Strub at the weather service. Or better still, have her live in the WCCO-radio studio for up-to-the-minute details of the outside weather.

I can hear them now. "Molly is slightly nervous and thunderstorms are reported at Rapid City." "Molly is breathing hard, storms are in process at Redwood Falls." "Molly has eagerly accepted her tranquilizers. Heavy rains and locally damaging winds reported in the Minnetonka area." If they looked around and found Molly missing, then a tornado warning should be broadcast. She's too smart to go through one of those again.

August, 1968

*"...when their feet touch sugar water...
their tongue automatically shoots out."*

RED, WHITE, AND REAR ADMIRALS

Every once in a while it's good to reminisce, and the other day we were doing just that on the occasion of our thirtieth wedding anniversary. As a family, we have had some fine times on Lake Minnetonka and one of the "times" was when we collected butterflies over a three-year period. I asked my youngest son what he remembered best about the collecting and he replied it was the catching of rear admirals.

As a navy man, I know full well what a real rear admiral is; but if there's a doctor in the house, I want him to know that I also know full well what his profession means when they speak of a rear admiral. My son misspoke, of course. He meant red admirals, a very pretty butterfly quite common to the Minnetonka area.

The other day I was walking along the Nicollet Mall when a fresh white admiral or banded purple butterfly coasted by. Last week, an equally fresh white admiral lay sunning itself — gently fanning its wings with a smile on its face, I suppose — right at the edge of our tennis court. This is unusual. The white admiral is common up north (Itasca, North Shore, Grand Rapids), but over the past many years I've seen very few of them around the Minnetonka area. As a matter of fact, I would guess we have more rear admirals than white admirals around the lake area.

Butterflies are something we tend to take for granted,

but in reality, they're marvelous creatures that are easy and fun to collect and study. Without any serious attempt to document them all, as a family we caught and mounted 41 different kinds of butterflies from an area of about two miles in and around the southwest end of Minnetonka. I'm sure there are people who still remember a bunch of long-legged towheads running like mad hither and yon through the fields and woods, seemingly tetched in the head by the noonday sun.

The red and white admirals are part of a butterfly family called Nymphalidae and are termed brush-footed butterflies because the front legs are very small and hairy and can't be used for walking. Like most other butterflies, when their feet touch sugar water or flower nectar, their tongue automatically shoots out. They "suck" in the fluid by contracting a part of their body which creates a vacuum that pulls the nectar up their hollow tongue into the mouth.

The red admiral is a common sight in July. Look for a butterfly about two inches across, black with curved red bands on its fore wings. He bobs and dips while flying and is a tough one to catch unless glutted on special food. His specific name is Vanessa atalanta and he can be found all over North America.

A close relation, Vanessa cardui, the Painted Lady or Thistle butterfly, has a population-explosion periodically. (The latest occurred in the spring of 1973 when huge numbers were observed migrating northward across Colorado. At a check point near Boulder, Colorado, Vanessa cardui was counted at a rate of 2 to 3 per second crossing a line 100 feet long. I saw numbers of them in Northern Montana later in the summer.)

The white admiral is not usually called by that name. His common name is the banded purple butterfly because of the deep purple color of the wings with a curved white band running across the fore wings. With a span of three inches, this butterfly sails when he flies, primarily because when he strokes his wings, they move downwards only to snap back to a horizontal position so all he can do is coast and sail. The scientific name for this white admiral is Basilarchia

White Admiral Butterfly

arthemis and it prefers the northern parts of our country. In our Twin City area, they frequent the tamarack bogs. One of these white admirals was seen at Lake Minnetonka on May 31, 1931, an all-time early date for Minnesota.

Midsummer is a great time for butterflies of all kinds. but especially the common monarch or milkweed butterfly. When you see a butterfly flitting around, take a good look at it. They come in a variety of colors, patterns, and sizes — all of them gorgeous. They're a part of our outdoors and the more you understand them, the more you appreciate the wonder of it all.

August, 1969

"Each raindrop acts as a tiny prism....
But, you see only one color from one drop...."

INSIDE THE RAINBOW

About two weeks ago we had a very pretty and refreshing evening shower, accompanied by dramatic pinky-red flowing clouds that were heading southeast. They literally pulsed from the light of the setting sun. I saw this from our west deck, and when I walked to the other side of the house and looked east across the upper lake, a gorgeous double rainbow had its north end bathing Island Park, its south end carressing Wawatasso Island. The Zimmerman Pass or Enchanted Island bridge was directly in the middle.

A good full double rainbow is hard to come by so I grabbed my Instamatic camera, and the developing produced a beautiful print. But the print also produced proof of what I thought I had seen and had never realized: the colors in the two rainbows were reversed with the lower bow going from violet on the inside to red on the outside, and the upper bow just the opposite.

And then I said to myself, just what is a rainbow? How is it formed? I've seen them all of my life and knew little about them. So, back to the books and a refresher course in a bit of physics. It's not enough to know about Judy Garland, the Wizard of Oz, and a pretty "Over the Rainbow" song; and it's not enough that rainbows have been called lots of things, like Arc of Light, Flashing Arch, Bow of Indra, Little Window in the Sky, Pride of the Rain, Arch of St. Martin, Bridge of

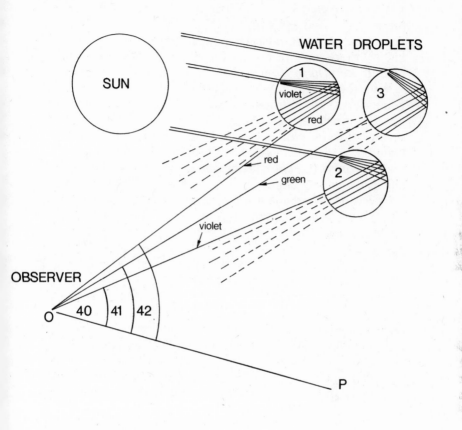

SUN

WATER DROPLETS

1

violet

red

3

red

green

2

violet

OBSERVER

O 40 41 42

P

(A) HOW A RAINDROP BREAKS
UP SUNLIGHT INTO COLORS

the Holy Spirit, Crown of St. Bernard, and the Girdle of God.

To have a rainbow, conditions must be just right, and the three basic conditions are: (1) the sun must be shining behind you; (2) there must be rain in the air in front of you; and (3) there must be a hazy, cloudy, and rainy background behind the rain in front of you.

With these right conditions, light from the sun in back of you enters the raindrops in front of you. Each raindrop acts as a tiny prism that breaks up the light beam into the basic seven colors of violet, indigo, blue, green, yellow, orange, and red, and bounces the broken-up light back out. But, you see only one color from one drop because each color has its own exact angle that it must enter your eye and each drop has its own angle in relation to your eye and the beam of sunlight. Red light enters your eye at about a 42 degree angle, green at about 41 degrees, and violet at about 40 degrees (See drawing A). The rainbow that you see has lots of colors because the air is full of drops but the banding is still determined by the angle to your eye.

The rainbow is bowed because you, the viewer, are really standing in the center of a cone with half the cone below the horizon and half above. The 42 degree red angle rays, for example, come at you from a semi-circle, and therefore you see the red rays as a bow or half a circle and the two ends of the half-circle end in the "pot of gold" as they touch the earth. Rainbows are usually from ½ to 1½ miles from your eye.

The amount of the different colors in a rainbow depends upon the size of the raindrops. The larger the drops, the more red there will be; the smaller the drops, the more violet. This is because the size of the drop affects the angle of the broken-up light as it leaves the drop. Large drops are about 1/20 inch in diameter.

A full rainbow always has two bows like the one I saw the other night, and the outer bow has its colors reversed from the inner bow. The primary inner bow is the smaller, the brighter, and the one you usually see. In drawing B, Bow I has the sunlight entering the drop, bouncing once, and then coming to your eye. Bow II, the secondary bow,

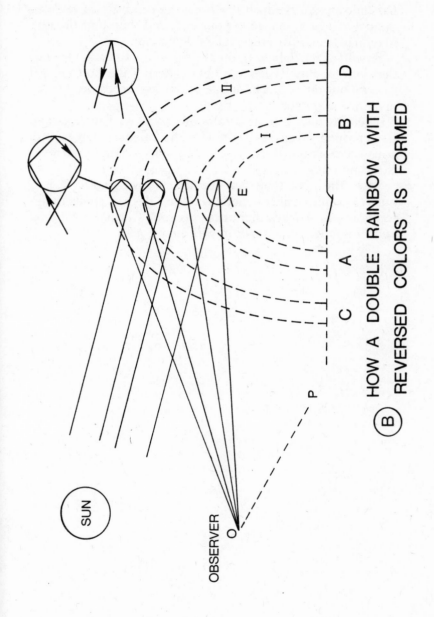

SUN

OBSERVER

B HOW A DOUBLE RAINBOW WITH REVERSED COLORS IS FORMED

225

has the sunlight bouncing twice in the drop which reverses the colors like an image in your eye, and therefore the rays reaching your eyes are reversed from Bow I.

Bow I has the light entering the top of the drop and leaving the bottom. Bow II has the light entering the bottom and coming out the top. These conditions are necessary for the angle to be proper for your eye.

The next time you see a rainbow, stand on your toes and then crouch down. You'll notice the rainbow moves with you, which is proof that the light angle striking your eyes is the important ingredient.

Also, the next time you see a rainbow, realize it is a marvelous physical concoction. I don't think it spoils things to know what makes them tick, do you? Certainly, I'll look at all rainbows from now on with new eyes.

August, 1971

*"A sewage plant basically does in six hours
what natural processes would do in five days."*

THE TREATMENT OF SEWAGE

A couple of weeks ago, I stood watching a recording pen marking a graph that was making a constant visual record of the number of gallons per minute of raw sewage that was coming into the Mound-Spring Park Sewage Plant for treatment. That afternoon, the graph showed a steady 1,000 gallons per minute being received from the 23 pump stations in the gathering system, plus the Hilltop School. It averaged about one million gallons in 24 hours. A recent rain was swelling the usual total by about 25 percent because of storm sewers and run-off.

After treatment in the sewage plant, the effluent or treated water is released from the sewage plant's final pond into a marsh that drains into Lake Langdon, then east through a culvert that runs under Highway 110 near Duane's 66 gas station into Lost Lake, from where a channel running south under the bridge at Highway 125 sends the effluent into Cook's Bay of upper Lake Minnetonka.

If the effluent daily average has been one million gallons (which would be high), then about one billion, 500 million gallons of effluent have been released into Minnetonka from this one source alone since this sewage plant opened for business June 16, 1964. This gallonage is equivalent to a little over four inches in the water level of the whole lake, or about one inch per year.

With all the hue and cry about water pollution, a sewage treatment plant is a handy whipping-boy and the plant at Mound is no exception. However, a little-known fact is that the Mound sewage plant is one of the most modern in the United States for its size, has a fine laboratory for daily control of the processes, and the effluent it does eventually discharge into the lake is infinitely sweeter than the sewage (much of it raw) that was getting into the lake only a short four years ago, before the new plant was in operation.

Leonard Kopp, Mound village manager, and Paul Farren, plant superintendent, gave me a thorough and technical tour of the sewage plant which operates on the "activated sludge" principle, a process originated in Sweden and put into practice in the United States by the Dorr-Oliver Co. under license. They built the Mound plant.

Farren is competent and complete in his knowledge of his plant, even though he's been in the sewage business only since the construction of this plant. Prior to this present job, he was a policeman in Mound for ten years. He celebrated his birthday on June 16, 1964, by starting up the sewage plant two days later than originally planned. Apparently it was rather exciting. The Tonka Toy plant started diverting its sewage into the new gathering system on June 16 at 10 A.M., but they weren't aware of the fact that the sewage plant still hadn't started to operate. Fortunately, it took about two hours for the stuff to arrive and by that time the plant was "on stream." Whew!

A sewage plant basically does in six hours what natural processes would do in five days. The raw sewage (99.9 percent water) from the gathering lines in the community enters the plant and goes through a grinder before processing. Coffee grounds are tough but so are the rocks, marbles, watches, ball-point pens, and even false teeth that have shown up in the sewage. Golf balls are the worst. Paul Farren can tell when a ball hits the grinder; the whole plant shakes.

The first main step in the treatment process is to "clarify" or separate the solids or sludge from the more liquid portion. The liquid goes one way, the sludge another.

The sludge from this first clarifier goes through a

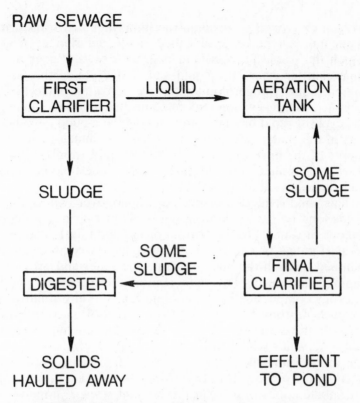

RAW SEWAGE

FIRST CLARIFIER → LIQUID → AERATION TANK

SLUDGE

SOME SLUDGE

DIGESTER ← SOME SLUDGE ← FINAL CLARIFIER

SOLIDS HAULED AWAY

EFFLUENT TO POND

SIMPLIFIED FLOW CHART OF MOUND SEWAGE PLANT

thickening and then a digester process where anaerobic bacteria (which don't need oxygen to live) take over in the sludge which is heated to 90 degrees F., and consume the waste. One by-product of this stage is methane or swamp gas (CH_4) which is used to heat the plant. Excess gas in the summer is burned outside as a flare. The end result of this part of the process is solid sludge which is trucked away and dumped.

The liquid from the first clarifier goes into a large aeration tank into which vast amounts of air are pumped to greatly accelerate the growth of aerobic bacteria (which need oxygen to live) who consume the impurities and transform them into a type of solid called "activated sludge" from which the whole process is named. This sewage goes to a final clarifier where the liquid and sludge are further separated. Some sludge, containing live activated bacteria, is fed back to the aeration tank in controlled amounts to keep the cycle of rapid bacterial growth going at a good clip. The rest of the sludge goes the way of the first sludge — to the mercy of the anaerobic bacteria. The liquid from the final clarifier is treated with chlorine to kill the aerobic bacteria and then flows into an effluent pond.

This pond is huge; it is seven feet deep, over two football fields long by one wide, and holds about fourteen million gallons of water. On the bottom of the pond lie 15,000 feet of perforated plastic air hose with lead weights. Air is pumped through the hose to aerate the water and promote rapid algae growth. The algae consume nitrogen and phosphorous compounds in the effluent and thereby remove a lot of them from the water. At the exit end of the pond, the effluent flows through a large plastic jug holding copper sulfate crystals which kill the algae as the effluent enters the marsh and Lake Langdon. When the treated effluent eventually overflows into Lake Minnetonka, the nitrate and phosphate concentration in the original sewage, hopefully, has been reduced by as much as 80 percent.

The last 20 percent of the nitrate-phosphate compounds remaining in the effluent is a difficult portion to get. To remove in excess of 90 percent of the original is extremely costly, and it's doubtful whether any process will ever be devised to economically remove 100 percent.

Although the main metropolitan sewer plant is now collecting the majority of the sewage effluent from around Lake Minnetonka, there will always be places where relatively small sewage treatment plants will be needed. The one at Mound is a good one, until some new concepts are developed. It will take a major breakthrough to make much of an improvement.

August, 1968

*"...last year his station netted and banded
92 different Baltimore Orioles....
This year only 32...."*

TIME FLIES WITH THE BIRDS

I remember back several years to when my father died. His last days were spent propped up in bed with a splendid view of our upper Lake Minnetonka. To see the lake, he looked over and past a series of 5-by-7 color enlargements of boy-hood scenes in Tottingham, London, England, that I had snapped for him that spring — scenes he hadn't seen for more than sixty years.

It was July 24 when he died, and at eight that evening literally hundreds of purple martins congregated at our garden martin house, clouds of raucous birds whirling and sailing and dipping as if in salute to a man who had fished and boated the lake for many years. As I remember it, the next day the martins were gone; they reappeared briefly in early August and then left for good.

Off and on since then, I've had the feeling that the martins always leave very early in August, but certainly not this year. I have been carefully documenting the martin activity in our dock martin house and as late as Sunday evening, August 23, the thirteen occupants of the house were still there. Monday morning, the twenty-fourth, they were gone and I haven't seen them since.

Why did they leave? Dragonflies and other insects were still plentiful, the weather hadn't been nearly as cold as it was when they arrived near the middle of April, and the second hatch of young haven't been flying so long that they really are fully prepared to head south on any kind of sustained flight.

The whys and wherefores of migration — the timing, the routes, and the returns — are subjects of great research and knowledge, but is so frustrating because the new research continually contradicts the old rather than substantiates it. The banding of birds has to be the main approach to someday unlocking the mysteries of migration.

Last weekend, I made what is becoming an annual visit to bird banding station No. 9877 located on the eastern shore of Lake Hubert north of Brainerd. Nestled among the pines and spruces, a retired executive from First National Bank of Minneapolis has turned his intelligence, interest, time and drive into a detailed and very scientific hobby of banding birds for about six months of the year in northern Minnesota, and then spending the other half-year near Tucson, Arizona.

As owner of one of thirty-nine master banding stations in Minnesota, this bander is compiling bird movement information. Like most things, the more involved he gets, the more he realizes how little we know of such things as bird migration and details of so many of the common daily habits of the birds.

For instance, last year his station netted and banded 92 different Baltimore orioles (amazing, being so far north and in the deep woods, but on a lake). This year only 32 have been caught. Apparently the birds were around, but because of constant high winds their flight patterns and habits changed enough to reduce the catch. This seems to have been a general pattern for the birds up there this year. To date this year, this bander has recorded 57 species of birds, compared to 60 last year, but the number of birds caught totals 390, down 40 percent from last year. Also, there has been an extensive worm infestation of trees in Northern Minnesota. With this ample supply for food, the birds weren't visiting his feeders as much and therefore were not being caught.

- Another unusual thing happened just three weeks ago.

Banding station #9877 with bird weighing scale

September 2 the mist nets were set but not one bird was around. Suddenly, in a five-minute period, 42 warblers were netted, and then for the rest of the day not one more bird was caught. Furthermore, these warblers were a mixed group composed of the following species: nashville, wilsons, black and white, golden wing, bay-breasted, black-throated green, chestnut-sided, canada, yellow, tennessee, myrtle, and blackburnian. Just as I arrived Saturday, a myrtle warbler had been caught. This is one of my favorite birds with its perky habits and bright yellow rump patch as it flits about.

This year, I was especially interested in this bander's feat of netting a total of nine different kingfishers. This can be called a feat when you realize that only five were banded in our entire state last year and only two others were recorded throughout the whole western United States. In some other banding years, Minnesota recorded two in 1967, one in 1968, and nine in 1969.

Of these nine kingfishers banded at Lake Hubert, four were of this year's hatch and five were hatched in previous years. The first one was netted July 17 and the last one August 30, although kingfishers will stay until the lake freezes. An interesting thing is that not one of the birds caught and banded has been recaptured, which shows that they must learn after the first time to avoid the mist net which my friend had strung out on his dock over the water.

A kingfisher is one of the heaviest birds that my friend has caught and banded. These nine averaged from 155 to 160 grams each (.03527 grams per ounce so they were about 5 ½ ounces in weight), which is heavy for a bird. They have weak feet which makes them hard to catch as they don't grab the mist net with their claws as do the usual perching birds. When weighing and measuring these nine birds, he found that the young birds had longer bills (the longest was 52 millimeters or a bit over two inches long) while the older birds had bills as much as ¼ inch shorter. This leads to the speculation that the bill wears down as they grow older, but no mention of this has been found in any literature.

By the end of October, this banding station on Lake Hubert will close up and move south for the winter, similar to the movement of most of the birds before the snow flies and the water freezes. My friend asked me to mention that if anybody ends up with a banded bird, he should record the event in detail and send the information and band to: Bird Banding Laboratory, Migratory Bird Populations Station, Fish and Wildlife Service, Laurel, Maryland 20810. For all you know, it might be one of his friends.

August, 1969
September, 1971

"Raccoons...have a lower jaw that articulates with their skull by means of a vertical rod. They can only move their mouth up and down like a dog."

THE CHOICE RACCOON

While boating with my wife Monday evening, I asked her what her choice would be for the bird to represent Minnetonka. She chose the wood duck and so would I. When asked about her plant candidate, she came up with purple loosestrife — and again we agreed. Finally, her animal choice was asked and she didn't hesitate to put the finger on the raccoon. I would too.

When you think about it, the coming of man around our lake has driven most animals away — the deer, the bear, the beaver, the fox, the mink and such (although a few of each still cling here and there) — but not the raccoon. Here's an animal that seems to thrive on the ways of man, turns them to his advantage, and ends up better off than in the good old days. Even though the raccoon was the symbol of the Whig party in the United States between 1838 and 1844, I would still welcome it as the animal symbol of urbanized Minnetonka and the resilience of an animal species.

Over our many years in the Lake Minnetonka area, we've had all kinds of raccoon experiences, but one of the most recent involved Sarah and Abraham. Our neighbors down the shore are on the Como Zoo list to raise animal babies and last year inherited two new-born raccoons which they promptly named Sarah and Abraham. They kept detailed records on their weights, eating habits, how long they stayed blind and such until they were capable of being turned loose outside. Sarah deserted the easy life last fall when some gay blade whistled her into the woods for good — and she has perhaps been seen once since.

Abraham stayed around, became close friends with Barney the dog and, when winter set in, took up residence under the boathouse near the Halsteds Bay shore. I haven't heard about him this summer because our friends are away for a while, but late in the winter, on a nice warm day, Abraham decided to stir a little and came crawling up the bank to the back door of the house. He stretched and yawned, threw up on the porch, ambled down the bank and went to sleep again. What a way to spend the winter!

Raccoons are part of the animal order Carnivora, as they eat flesh as well as vegetable matter and have a lower jaw that articulates with their skull by means of a vertical rod. They can only move their mouth up and down like a dog. As a matter of fact, the raccoons are part of that group that includes cats, dogs, bears, seals, walruses, mongooses, pandas and most of our other animals like skunks and weasels.

The raccoon is the only Minnesota representative of the family Procyonidae and is of the genus Procyon lotor. The average weight of a grown raccoon is about eighteen pounds, although they have been taken as heavy as thirty-five pounds. They grow up to three feet long, have very long legs and sharp claws making them expert climbers, and have six or seven rings in their tails. They love the nighttime hours and prefer low lands, and river and stream banks. They are found as far north as there are oaks. A low acorn crop seriously cuts into the population of the raccoon. Their gestation period is sixty-three days and they have from two to six young ones around the first of May. By mid-August they are pushing three months old and, in conjunction with the corn season, are as active as the dickens they are. The males wander around and pretty much ignore the family, but the females stay with the young for almost a year, finding food, training them in the arts of climbing and robbing garbage cans, and knocking down corn stalks to get at the

Raccoon

ears with ease. The females have been known to take in orphaned raccoons and treat them as their own.

One of our favorite remembrances of raccoons occurred several years ago. While sleeping on our porch on a marvelous big swinging bed, we were awakened one morning just at daybreak by a mother raccoon and five little ones. She was up a big red cedar not ten feet from us and the young ones were up a large cottonwood fifty feet away — up and unable to get down. They whimpered and cried like human babies until Mom ambled down and over and up and carefully led them to safety on the ground. We remember this happening especially, because the red cedar was a close friend and the 1965 tornado tore it out by its roots, depositing it at the foot of the same big cottonwood.

This is the time of year for the raccoons to be on the move, and more and more of them are seen killed on the highways. They love that corn as a welcome change from the frogs and crabs and fruits and berries they usually eat.

A while back, one was at my duck feeder in the dark when my golden retriever Molly and I came along to add some corn. You've never heard such snarling and hissing and carrying on until the dark body jumped in the lake and swam into the darkness.

It's a special joy to experience that kind of wildness in the midst of our rapidly changing environment. I hope they stay around.

July, 1970

"This new strain of wild rice is non-shattering, which means that the seeds stay on the stalk until...ripe...."

WILD RICE IS NICE

If you do this sort of thing, the conventional wild rice harvesting season opened the last week in August for a period of nine days, ending tomorrow. During this time, only five days are legal and during those days, only a grand total of twelve hours is the permitted harvesting time.

It won't be long before the old way of harvesting wild rice is a thing of the past. Two things have happened during the past few years, things that are harbingers of a possible major crop for northern Minnesota.

One is that a new strain of wild rice has been developed and before too many years will be at its peak of perfection. This new strain is non-shattering, which means that the seeds stay on the stalk until most of them are ripe, instead of ripening from the top down and "shattering" or dropping as they ripen, making it necessary to harvest a rice area several times to get a decent crop. The second thing is the development of rice fields or rice paddies for efficient crop management, and mass-harvesting with mechanical equipment because the non-shattering strain allows for a single harvest.

In 1970, paddy wild rice produced more poundage than lake or stream wild rice for the first time. 1971 saw 10,000 acres of rice paddies and the estimate for 1972 is that almost 20,000 acres will be under cultivation. A paddy acre will produce nearly 200 pounds of green wild rice, compared to the 40 or 50 pounds retrieved from wild growing areas.

The result is that as the years pass by, more and more wild rice will be grown, the price will stabilize at a lower price per pound than in the past, and a national and international market can be tapped.

Minnesota is the number one wild rice producer, but almost 75 percent of the crop has been consumed in Minnesota, half of that in the Twin Cities area. We take wild rice for granted, but only 2 percent of the people in the United States know of it or have used it. Think what they've missed, with no wild rice in duck, pheasant or cornish hen stuffing, no wild rice hot dishes, or no steaming wild rice with butter and salt along with roast duck, or under beef stroganoff.

Earlier this year, it was anticipated that the price of wild rice would be down because of increased production. Then the rains came and the recent flooding in north-central Minnesota has dashed the 1972 hopes of many a wild rice farmer.

A call to Lunds supermarket Tuesday morning substantiated the expected shortage. Last year's No. 1 wild rice retail price was $3.98 per pound. At present, the price is $4.39 but this is expected to rise as the '72 crop comes in as a big disappointment. (Note: A last-minute unexpected supply came on the market and the price dropped to $3.50 per pound.)

Half of the people in the world depend upon rice as their main food. There are eight thousand varieties of rice in India alone but almost all commercial white rice comes from the strain Oryza sativa. Wild, Canada or Indian rice is an annual grass called Zizania aquatica. Rice is a grass, as are timothy, hay, wheat, corn, sugar cane, and bamboo. Clover and alfalfa are not grasses. Grains are grasses that are grown mostly for food.

Northern Beltrami County in northern Minnesota is called the "Wild Rice Capital of the World." The Ojibways called the wild rice "manomin" meaning "good grain," and I suppose Mahnomen, Minnesota, in the White Earth Indian

Reservation up north is a derivative. Menominee, Wisconsin, is supposed to have been named in a similar fashion. Because most of the wild rice comes from Minnesota, it's only natural that the paddy-type of cultivation was developed by a Minnesotan named Frank Kosbau who lives in a little town named Waskish at the east end of Upper Red Lake on the Red Lake Indian Reservation. (I pass through Waskish in the fall on my way to Canada; it's easy to miss unless you slow down.)

I have a map of Lake Minnetonka made by the Army Corps of Engineers and published in 1905. On it are defined two areas of wild rice. One is between Deering Island and the east point of the Seton Lake channel, and the other is along the northern shore of Harrison Bay.

The local game warden of a few years ago told me he has seen some wild rice in the "Little Venice" area of dredged

Rotating ovens mass-parch dried rice

channels southeast of the Narrows near West Point; someplace I've seen an old picture of the Narrows channel itself that looked full of wild rice; but the closest current stand of wild rice seems to be up in Anoka County. There's a small stand near Waterville (per Dr. John Moyle) but in general, wild rice is rare south of St. Cloud and Stearns County except for some along the Mississippi River as far south as Winona.

There are about 125 major wild stands of wild rice in the state and thousands of smaller ones, along with at least 96 lakes and marshes that are called "Rice Lake". I hunt ducks on one of them north of Perham but rather than being a true lake, it is really a widening of the Ottertail River.

With the new non-shattering breed of wild rice, and the technique of paddy growing, even the Indians are switching to the new methods. Leech Lake, Red Lake and Nett Lake Indians are getting into the new ways, but apparently the Mille Lacs Indians haven't as yet. The "useless" big marsh north and east of Aitkin (the area of the ancient Glacial Lake Aitkin) has several big paddy operations. By the way, the word "paddy" means rice in Malayan.

So, like all things, changes are coming to our wild rice. Several by-products of paddy cultivation have come to light, however. The paddies help in spring water flood control (though apparently not severe summer rains), give ducks great breeding areas, and northern pike find them beautiful spawning grounds. The Indians have been fearful that new methods and excess production will hurt or totally kill off their source of wild rice income. The rains helped them this year by holding down production but they will have to modernize. It's good that some of them have done so already. Wild rice is such a good food that nobody should be hurt by changes or improvements in its growth and harvesting. It seems to me that wild rice presents a perfect major-crop solution to northern Minnesota industry woes. Imagine the pounds of wild rice that could be used by the 212 million people in America alone.

August, 1972

SUMMER ENDS EARLY

I think the summer of 1970 came to an end at precisely 11:15 P.M. Friday, August 14.

It happened quite dramatically. Starting about the first of August, we had a steady stretch of hot, humid weather and many of the days gave us a kind of smog because of a temperature layering called an inversion. Leading up to the night of August 14, the barometer slowly dropped until it was reasonably low at about 29.70. Referring to the diagram, it is clear how the weather front came through at about 11:15 P.M. and the barometric pressure jumped almost straight up 10 points. Then, visualize summer fighting a losing battle for almost six hours while a whole series of fronts rolled through (remember that continuous thunder and tremendous lightning?) until at 5:15 A.M. Saturday the thing was over and the pressure started a nice easy rise to good weather.

From that day on, the air has been fresh, the nights cool, and everybody says "It feels just like fall, doesn't it?"

Officially a summer season doesn't end until September 21 or so. The reason rests in the lap of our world. The earth's axis is tilted exactly 23 degrees 27 minutes away from being perpendicular to its orbit around the sun. The result is that the earth "wobbles" as it goes around and around in relation to the sun. Twice a year during this wobbling, the axis of the earth is at right angles to the sun and the length of days and nights are most equal. In the fall, this period is called the autumnal equinox and although the popular idea is that it happens on September 21, this is not always the case. For instance, in 1972, the exact time of the autumnal equinox was at 5:33 P.M., C.D.T., September 22. The length of that day was 12 hours, 10 minutes (with an even 12 hours on the 26th).

But to me, this relationship of the earth to the sun is only one of the final changes that have occurred in moving from summer to fall.

The nights are cooler, and with soil and water temperatures generally warmer than the early morning air, fog and mist plague the airlines and drivers on their way to work. It is a beautiful sight, however, to have the rising sun light up low-hanging veils of mist in the low spots.

Some of our summer bird friends are gone. The purple martins have taken off for points south. I haven't seen an oriole for almost that long, and the number of grackles has diminished though some are still here.

I always feel a little sad to see the corn season about over. The fields are mature and the corn you buy is either too young or too old and not "just right," like at the peak of the season. My garden is overflowing with eggplant and squash, the tomatoes have peaked, onions are beautiful, and

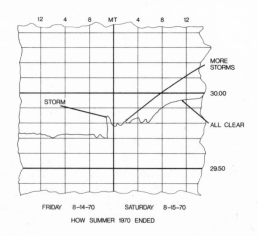

HOW SUMMER 1970 ENDED

the cucumbers are nearly through — all signs of fall.

A welcome fact of late summer is that the growth rate of grass has lessened and the crabgrass has slowed, going to seed. The pretty tinges of color in some maples and the sumac hint of things to come, the mum plants and their blooms are smashing, and the willow trees have their leaves "bronzing" before falling in the high winds to come.

Further signs of summer's end: the leaves on my Engelman Ivy vines are withering and the immature berries are more obvious, soon to turn blue and give the birds a real treat; a velvet-soft fresh mourning cloak butterfly nearly landed on my tennis racquet last Saturday and a fairly rare black swallowtail butterfly stayed with me in the garden while I picked a few over-ripe beans.

There's a variety of wildflowers along the shore. As I stepped off the dock Sunday, a hummingbird by-passed the profusion of orange blooms of the butter and eggs plant to hover over the flat tops and white blooms of the white snakeroot. I couldn't detect any particular odor to the snakeroot bloom and under the glass the bloom was pretty like all blooms but nothing so striking as to necessarily attract the hummingbird. I guess the bird knows something we don't know.

Despite boat leakage, battery troubles, peeling varnish, and the general disrepair of a boat late in the season, a pleasant boat ride around the lake showed all kinds of signs that summer was ending. Few boats were out, probably because most boaters were watching an early pro football game on television. Fishing is getting better and a boat with a father and two sons excitedly pulled in a three-pound Northern as we passed them. Further on, a boat with four adults netted a nice bass as we chugged by. We must bring pretty good luck!

Several young blue herons were spotted and recalled to us that this year is one of the better blue heron years. As we boated along the shores, they would land ahead of us, only to fly again as we approached. Sunday morning, I watched as a blue heron landed on a buoy, the first time I've ever seen that happen. Being part German, I couldn't help but wonder what a damen would land on.

The final straw vote to determine how close fall is in coming is to take water temperatures as the surface waters are gradually cooling off. It's always surprising to me how different the "profile" of water temperatures is from year to year. Note how the surface and deep water temperatures vary within these three years. It's true there's a two-week period covered by these three sets of readings but the intent is to bracket September 1. Surface temperatures may cool off during a two-week's span, but deeper water temperatures wouldn't change materially. A general conclusion can be that September 1 waters at the Pass have an average surface reading of 70 degrees and 50 degrees in the deeps. Wind direction and strength of the wind has the greatest effect on temperatures from 15 feet in depth to the surface. Bottom temperatures are pretty much determined by the depth of water mixing in the springtime.

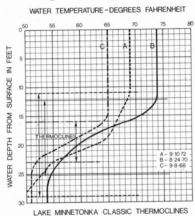

WATER TEMPERATURE—DEGREES FAHRENHEIT

LAKE MINNETONKA CLASSIC THERMOCLINES

I'm sure all of us hate to have summer come to an end, primarily because it's one more summer into the history books. We Minnesotans are lucky, though, with the gorgeous fall colors that are coming, the crisp nights, and Indian Summer days. When you come right down to it, every one of our seasons is terrific. How lucky can we be.

August, 1968

Part 4

THE FALL SEASON
September through November

*"It can dive...so fast that pellets from a
shotgun, when fired from sixty yards, whiz by
the empty spot...occupied an instant before."*

THE NOT-SO-CRAZY LOON

When doing business in a foreign country, especially Europe, it's appropriate to carry gifts with you from your home territory. I've traveled the Continental route enough times that the choosing of a different but distinctly-Minnesota present has become a real problem.

My last swing, however, was successful from the gift standpoint. I took a number of prints of the official picture of our state bird, the loon, done by Les Kouba. He was nice enough to autograph the prints for me, so at each business stop, the presentation of the picture did its expected job.

I've always loved the loon. To me, the lonely call, the distinctive flight, and the dapper look of the mature bird on the water is pure Minnesota. But beyond all that, the loon is an amazing bird and in a class by itself.

My daily notes of this summer state that when playing tennis on Saturday morning, July 20, two loons flew over, calling to each other. This marked their arrival back to Minnetonka after nesting elsewhere, and welcome back they always are. They stay with us until the lake freezes over.

The loon's scientific name is *Gavia immer immer* (our Common Loon). He is a lousy walker and only a fair flyer, but a superb swimmer.

I've never seen a loon on land, have you? Apparently this is a rarity, and for good reasons. Their legs are set far back on the body, which affects their balance on land. Also, most of the leg is structurally tucked into the body and only the lower tarsus portion is extended and usable. The legs are short and stubby.

When a loon moves around on land, it's by hopping and using the wings as crutches. Their nests are on land, or at least above the water, but always by deep water so the bird can slip into and under the water immediately.

Comparing a loon's heavy body weight (in grams) to its small wing area (in square centimeters), the ratio is only 0.5, whereas a golden crowned kinglet's ratio is 8.87. This is why a loon has a dickens of a time taking off from the water, sometimes requiring up to a quarter of a mile to get up. Once airborne, they circle to gain altitude much like an airplane but rarely fly higher than 400 feet or so in the air — usually only 100 feet high. Most of the time you see them flying singly or in pairs, but I saw seven flying together and yodeling in chorus only two weeks ago north of Brainerd.

The loon's flight speed is about 60 m.p.h. and the short wings are so powerful that they make a whistling sound during each short beat. When coming in for a landing, loons lower their short legs like wheels and plow the water surface for an initial distance to cut the high flight speed they had to maintain during landing to keep their heavy bodies airborne.

They're in their true element when on, or under, the water. The body is built around solid heavy bones covered with muscle and the dark flesh of divers. (The dark tone is due to a special hemoglobin of the blood to supply oxygen during dives.) The body feathers are super dense.

On the water, a loon is beautiful. I've watched many of them through my 25-power spotting scope and they all seemed dressed and ready for a ball. Apparently there is no easy way to tell the sex of a loon. Plumage, calls, size, and normal behavior are much the same. Sometimes they'll lay their heads flat on the water and paddle around as if snorkeling (maybe they are!). Other times they roll part-way over with one leg in the air and their white belly can be seen way across the lake. A wonder of nature is that day-old loon chicks do the same thing!

The Common Loon

When diving, the loon is a master. It can somehow, at will, change its specific gravity and quietly sink under the water, sometimes with only a tiny portion of the head showing. It can dive with a forward kick of the neck and an easy but quick arching of the body. A dive is accomplished so fast that pellets from a shotgun, when fired from sixty yards, whiz by the empty spot the loon occupied an instant before. On close observation, the loon's feathers compress just before diving to drive out the air between the feathers. Nature thinks of everything.

Under the water, even a fast trout respects the loon. Using its legs for locomotion and its wings for steering, the loon looks like, and moves at the speed of, a fish. It usually stays under water for around forty-five seconds, but has been clocked for as long as three minutes. One unsolved mystery is how a loon can dive as deep as 250 feet and not suffer the "bends." Fishermen have netted loons that deep, and many baited deep set-lines have hooked loons as they grabbed the minnows. Apparently, the loon can regulate its circulation of blood to the muscles so its oxygen requirements are greatly reduced. It can also store the manufactured carbon dioxide in its body during prolonged dives without bad effects.

I don't know about you, but instead of thinking how crazy a loon can be, I will always think how wonderful, marvelous, and mysterious a creature the loon is — a welcome part of the sights and sounds of our Magnificent Minnesota.

September, 1968

*"What you see under the microscope is...
a game that is played by rules we don't
understand."*

A NEW KIND OF GAME

Watching sports on television has become a pastime that
threatens to become fulltime. Even before the 160-odd game
schedule of baseball is over, football starts. Before football
really gets underway, hockey and basketball start. Football
sputters to a reluctant stop late in January, and before you
know it, baseball starts before hockey and basketball are
finished. Throw in dashes and pinches of tennis, golf, soccer,
skiing, wrestling, swimming, bowling, and even curling —
and it's a wonder the network finds a time slot for Rowan
and Martin to be as nutty as they are.

I have not been irretrievably hooked by the hypnosis of
television, so it wasn't any hardship to switch allegiance from
it to the viewing of the drama of life through another form
of glass, the microscope. My wife may sometimes feel the
way the cartoon depicts it, but it does make the point that
watching water samples is a fascinating business, and time
has a way of slipping by.

What you see under the microscope is a new kind of game,
a game that is played by rules we don't understand. I suppose
we could regard ourselves as members of some sort of a
watery football team because we have lake problems we're
trying to tackle, potential ills we're trying to guard against,
green water we hope to end, and a concern that brings these
problems to the front and center. Our backfield has been

pretty weak because nobody to date has found a way to take the ball and run with it. Maybe with some aggressive signal calling, a few end runs, and a couple of long bombs (of the proper type), we can start scoring against the very offensive team of green that has been giving our Lake Minnetonka a bad time.

This opponent of ours is an all-star bunch, a team of pros that can boast of thousands and thousands of years of experiences playing the game their way. They can easily spoil our plays (and play) when we least expect it, red-dog (or green-dog?) our backfields and our front lake shores in spite of our defenses, foul up our pleasures and propellors, and rarely get penalized, no matter how mean or green they become.

The names and colors of these players are probably as unfamiliar to you as are most of the names put up for grabs in an expansion draft. But take it from me, they play their positions well and must be respected. The green and blue-green algae show their own colors, and the amber and gold of the diatoms add their dash of hues, much like stripes and large numerals on human uniforms. Quarterback *Alphanizomenon flos-aquae* seems to be in on every play throughout the year, and apparently was the big gun in the very green water sample I brought back from Lake of the Woods a few weeks ago. A trio of fleet backs complete a backfield that keeps on the move and adds variety to the plays you watch under the scope. These three are "old chicken-foot" *Ceratium hirundinella, Keratella quadrata,* and "one-eye" Cyclops.

The forward line is a rough one. *Oscillatoria rubescens* makes a couple of fine ends, long, thin and colorful. Microcystis and Coelosphaerium are a couple of huge tackles hard to get around. The Anabaena twins, *spiroides* and *flos-aquae,* guard the inside of the line with their entangling play. The center of attention on many a move is the final member of the team — Stephanodiscus, so round, so firm, so fully packed.

It's apparent to me that if we're going to take on a major team that plays games with our lake, stream, and river problems, our team has to be first class: the best of players,

"What's happened to us, George? I remember when you
used to look at _me_ that way."

Drawing by F. B. Modell; © 1968
The New Yorker Magazine, Inc.

the best in equipment, and the best arena. Surely, it costs money, lots of it, but millions are spent for a pro sports franchise and its operating expenses are in the hundreds of thousands of dollars every year. The game we must play, this new kind of game, is at a point where we must play for keeps or throw in the towel. I happen to love a good tough contest and never start a game without hoping I'm going to win. We're all going to win the contest against our environmental problems. When your time comes, be sure to buy your own season ticket. It will be the best investment you've ever made.

October, 1968

"The banding of birds...is a basic ingredient in the scientific study of bird migration."

BANDING AND MIGRATION

There's a young male downy woodpecker who undoubtedly complained to its mother or father the other day that it's hard to eat in peace nowadays.

For the second time in six days, he was trapped while tearing away at a large chunk of suet, examined, weighed, recorded, and then turned loose. From the squawks and chatter he let out while being handled, I think he had a better idea of what he, and we, could be doing at that moment. He didn't know it, but he was trapped for the purpose of being banded.

I have known about banding and the tremendous amount of knowledge that has been gained through the diligent work of volunteers and professional banders around the United States and the world, but I had never witnessed an actual trapping and recording operation.

It's fascinating to see just how the very fine mist nets are set out, made of string as delicate as old-fashioned hair nets, and black, so the net is nearly invisible when strung across an opening by the woods, or between water and some feeders. With little or no wind, the net is motionless, and its size — up to eight feet tall and twenty feet wide — makes it pretty tough for a bird not to be caught as it flies along.

As a bird hits the net, it immediately becomes entangled because, about every eighteen inches, a heavier weave of string causes other lighter string to fold and collapse, en-meshing the bird. These nets must be checked every ten minutes or so, so no harm comes to the birds. The high metabolism rate of birds coupled with their frantic antics in the net would kill them after a relatively short period.

Other ways to trap birds include equipping various feeding stations with trap doors that are tripped either by the weight of the bird or by hand from a safe distance.

The downy woodpecker that we caught was in a suet feeder with a bottom trap door that opened inward to let the bird in, but then dropped shut when he started to eat the suet and tripped the trap. He didn't become concerned after being trapped until my friend's hand came into the feeder to catch him.

There's a special way to hold a bird in your hand for good examination — on his back in your partially closed palm with his head sticking back and out between two of your middle fingers. This exposes his body, legs, and what have you to full view, but keeps his beak away and out of harm's reach.

A bird bander must be very methodical and accurate, and it's a compliment with a vote of confidence to have a full permit to do bird banding. Catching a bird is only the first step. The age, sex, species, condition, and weight of the bird must be determined and recorded. If the bird hasn't been banded before, one of six sizes of aluminum bands is care-fully clamped around a leg, and the number of the band entered into a logbook along with the other data. Then the bird is carefully released, none the worse for the experience except for a ruffled composure matching some of the feathers.

The banding of birds to check their various habits is a basic ingredient in the scientific study of bird migration. It's amazing that a final explanation of why and how the urge to migrate gets into the birds has not been found. Theories by the dozens have been dreamed up but, without exception, for one reason or another they all have been shot down. One idea is the northern home theory, which main-tains that birds were gradually forced south by the Ice Age

MISSISSIPPI FLYWAY

and now go back north in warm weather and south in cold weather. The southern home theory says birds started in the south, were forced north by over-population, were checked by the Ice Age, and now travel north and south according to the weather. The photoperiodism concept bases migration movements on the length of daylight and food availability. A fourth main hypothesis is the continental drift idea which proposes that eons ago there were two widely separated continents north and south and the birds traveled to and fro and still do.

When birds migrate is a puzzler, too. Some leave early in the year when there's still lots of food. Some remain later than any smart bird should. Some travel in daylight, some travel only at night. In general, it is the smaller birds that fly at night for protection during the long trips. Because their food requirements are high, they eat during the day and fly when food isn't readily available.

During the fall migration of birds, any of us could find a bird with a band on its leg. If you find one of these birds, either dead or alive, make a note of your name and address, the letters and numbers on the band, the date, town, county, and state when and where found, and say how the bird was found — dead, shot, trapped or what have you — and send this data to:

Bird Banding Office
Patuxent Wildlife Research Center
U. S. Fish and Wildlife Service
Laurel, Maryland.

If the bird is dead, it is helpful to send in the leg band. They will return the band to you if you so request it.

You will also receive a report of the original banding of the bird. I know it will give you a feeling of belonging, of helping, of adding one more piece to a gigantic puzzle. It's everybody's mystery. Imagine a blue-wing teal that traveled from northern Canada to Venezuela in just one month — a distance of 3,800 miles! — proven by a band on its leg.

October, 1968
September, 1970

*"...the lake does have her own way of refreshing
the water....Turnover of the water in the fall
is the saving grace...."*

BASEMENT-CLEANING TIME

In spite of tin cans, aluminum cans, and disposable no-return
bottles, each fall our basement at the Pass has collected a
remarkable array of miscellaneous beer, low-calorie and odd
brands of pop bottles in 8, 10, 12, 14 and 16-ounce capacities.
I return what bottles I can to the store for refunds, but the
rest of the stuff I chuck in the garbage can.

Along with these unwanted bottles go empty cartons, torn
and soaked life jackets, chipped and broken clay pots, empty
bug spray cans, an odd beat-up gardening glove and maybe
even a tennis racket whose frayed strings finally gave out
and could no longer hold the wooden frame in a semblance
of shape.

Humans clean their basements come fall — but so do
most lakes. Minnetonka cleans hers very regularly and
energetically. True, our lake can't remove the multitudes
of beer cans, bottles, bait cans, watches, anchors, glasses,
screwdrivers, and countless other objects tossed into the
lake or lost overboard during a long hard summer — but
the lake does have her own way of refreshing the water and
preparing for winter.

Each spring and fall, the water in Minnetonka, and in
lakes like it, "turns over" — bottom water, no matter how
deep, is circulated to the top and top water goes to the
bottom. These two turnovers each year earn Minnetonka

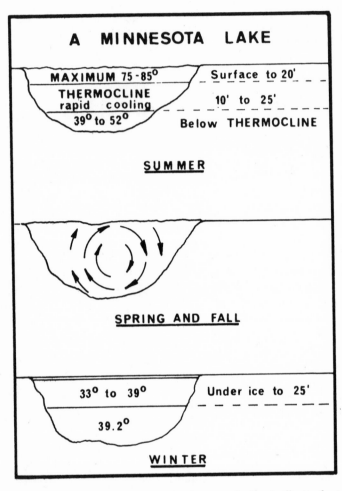

A MINNESOTA LAKE

MAXIMUM 75-85°   Surface to 20'

THERMOCLINE
rapid cooling   10' to 25'

39° to 52°   Below THERMOCLINE

SUMMER

SPRING AND FALL

33° to 39°   Under ice to 25'

39.2°

WINTER

a second-class dimictic lake rating, and that's first class in anybody's book.

Turnover of the water in the fall is the saving grace for our type of lake. Without it, fish would die, ice would be solid from top to bottom, weeds would rot and our lake would be a strange thing indeed. The turnover accomplishes two main things: It brings oxygen-rich surface water to the deeps for the long winter, while it brings oxygen-poor deep water to the surface for "recharging." The change in the specific gravity of water makes it possible to have a solid ice cap on the surface of the lake while having unfrozen water below to support lake life while the ice is present.

Actually, the whole principle of the water turnover and ice cap deals with water of unequal weight. A peculiarity of water is its specific gravity, or its weight per standard of measurement. It is heaviest at 39.2 degrees Fahrenheit and, therefore, lighter in weight when both warmer and cooler than this temperature. As our cool fall weather comes, the warm lighter summer surface water starts to cool, and the thermocline — that band of water where temperatures change rapidly from warm to cool as the water depth increases — shrinks in size until the upper water is about

WATER DENSITY

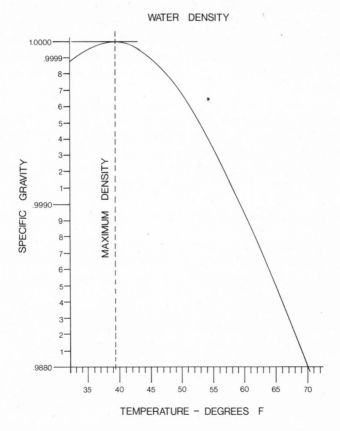

TEMPERATURE – DEGREES F

equal in temperature to the lower water which has been cooler and heavier all summer. This lower, cooler, heavier water has easily stayed under the warmer, lighter surface water, but now the weights of the two waters are approximately equal. As a result, winds, currents, and pressure changes cause a thorough mixing or turnover of the strata.

After the water has been thoroughly mixed, cooler weather continues to cool off the waters until 39.2 degrees is reached. Then the surface waters continue to be cooled, but as their temperatures go below 39.2 degrees, the water becomes lighter and lighter and deep mixing ceases.

The basement has been cleaned.

Taking temperatures in water at various depths is tricky and time-consuming unless special instruments are used. I use a "black box" slapped together at my office; it is a direct-reading thermistor-type of thermometer. With it, I can take readings at will at any depth in Minnetonka and have taken thirty readings in as short a time as five minutes.

The end of a long wire has a thermistor on it. A thermistor is a device whose ability to resist or conduct an electrical current changes depending upon its temperature. By using a flashlight battery to create a small electrical current, the changes in the thermistor can be shown or read out on a meter in the black box that is calibrated in degrees of temperature. The thermistor is much more sensitive to change than is the regular column of mercury in the normal thermometer.

Just exactly when the turnover starts in the fall depends primarily upon the strength of the winds to stimulate churning and the temperature of the water, but an average time for Minnetonka is usually late October to early November when the water has cooled to between 45 and 50 degrees. But we know the turnover will happen this year — and the next — and the next. If it doesn't, it's "good-bye" to our lakes. That's why I feel like saying a cheery "hello" to the turnover when it does happen.

November, 1968

*"...it wasn't the time to write about the death
....of the lakes we love and enjoy so much...."*

FALL MOODS

Late Sunday afternoon I changed my mind about the subject matter of the upcoming column for that week.

I was going to write about the major effect man is having on our waters and how it relates to the past, present, and future.

My lead paragraph was going to describe the slow death of our lakes since their birth at the end of the last glacial age, and how the classic pattern of a lake dying was being followed by Minnetonka. Contamination from runoff and rainfall brings soil and nutrients to the water; weeds and algae grow and die and add muck and decayed vegetation to the bottom; plants, grasses, and trees gradually encroach along the shoreline; the lake gets shallower, turns into a marsh, and then becomes a shady forested glen or a barren prairie.

After this preamble, I was going to criticize Man a bit. I was going to say that without Man, this process of a lake dying would take thousands and thousands of years, but with Man, we're in danger of speeding up the process to the point where a thousand years become one. Through our ignorance and neglect we are robbing countless future generations of the pleasures of our water resources that all of us have been so privileged to enjoy.

But then on Sunday afternoon my two grandchildren

arrived to spend the rest of the day. The Gophers had achieved a tremendous upset over Purdue Saturday afternoon; the North Stars had overpowered the Detroit Red Wings Saturday night; the Vikings were in the process of licking the Packers that very afternoon; and the Pipers were destined to walk away with their game that night. With elections over, the international scene somewhat quiet, and even student demonstrations simmering down because of the long weekend and vacation on Armistice Day, suddenly it wasn't the time to write about the death of anything, especially that of the lakes we love and enjoy so much.

As I sat watching my two grandsons playing in front of the fire in the fireplace, a magnificent large-flake early snowfall was in progress. At the same time, black bodies of huge curly-tailed northern mallards barreled overhead with wings set as they zoomed down to the corn feeder. A friendly drop-in call of neighbors from down the shore added to the afternoon, especially because they were so enjoying the briskness of the air. They were unaware of the snowflakes still resting lightly on their eyebrows as they arrived. With all of that and lots more too, the immense joy of living became so acute that afternoon that I couldn't imagine at that moment how anything could be wrong.

It was not the time and place to remember that 90 million American cars today waste one out of ten gallons of gasoline to pollute the air with over two hundred different chemicals spewing from the exhausts, and that millions of cars elsewhere are making life so difficult — like in Tokyo, Japan, for example, where traffic policemen must retreat to relief stations every half-hour to breathe pure oxygen.

It was not the time to recall that until some corrective measures recently reduced the amount somewhat, New York City was throwing over 600,000 tons of sulfur into the air and onto itself each year. (I well remember St. Paul secretaries finding their nylons falling apart after the lunch hour because of sulfur compound fallout — and this was in the late 1940s.) And even though the thickly falling flakes of snow would be dampening any sounds of takeoff, it still was not the time to think of the 88 pounds of pollutants

THE AGING OF A LAKE

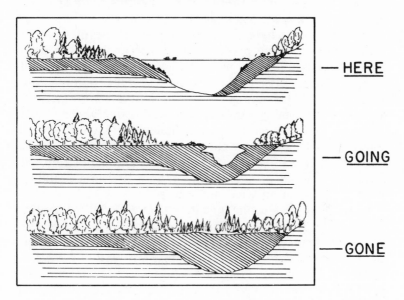

— <u>HERE</u>

— <u>GOING</u>

— <u>GONE</u>

that are pumped into the air every time a jet takes off (how many thousands of times each day?).

The spirit of that Sunday afternoon was determining my mood, but then, our lives are made of moods — physical, mental, political, economic — you name it. We may not want to admit it or maybe we're not aware of it, but as things change, we change, too. What we must do is realize there are changes and adjust and understand as they occur.

Just think of some of the recent changes of moods in our country. For years our economy was steaming along, buoyed by the confidence of a constantly rising stock market, billions pumped into the space program and the war — when suddenly the mood changed and here we are today, struggling, with everybody cautious and wondering.

It was only last spring that Earth Day had the populace stirred up about pollution. Today the problems and possibly the mood haven't changed, but certainly the pace has. There hasn't been a true change in the buying habits of housewives, with detergents and no-return bottles still being dispensed. And, to my knowledge at least, the schools are still concerned but don't have Earth Days planned again.

Everyday, existing problems grow larger and new problems are added to old problems. And whose fault is the environmental crisis? Our children's? Our parents' and grandparents'? Of course not — the blame is on our doorstep — yours and mine. The troubles of our waters, soils, and air is not somebody else's troubles — it's yours — and yours — and mine. How can anybody, regardless of age or description, stick their head in the sand like an ostrich and either say "What problem?" or "Whose problem?" and ignore the facts as to what and whom?

Here I am re-altering my mood, ending up by writing about those things that shouldn't disturb the mood of that precious Sunday afternoon. But it's only because I feel strongly about the duty — the obligation — that I have to the children coming along that I do my best to protect the environment, to help with the problems, to add to progress while not adding to its problems, and leave this beautiful world someday not in a worse shape than what I inherited but, hopefully, updated and maybe a little better.

Then, maybe the grandchildren of my grandsons will enjoy most of that which I've enjoyed. Just the thought makes me very happy.

November, 1970

*"...the wing primaries actually act like a
propeller on an airplane to pull the duck
forward...."*

PROPELLING DUCKS

While writing this column there are several hundred mallards and several dozen wood ducks wheeling around and down to my feeder deck: bodies suddenly appearing through the mist and fog to dip and dive and skim the water surface towards their daily ration of golden corn.

I love the ducks and what they stand for. Hardy birds that don't mind taking a handout under the circumstances but yet stay wild and independent — so much so that a passing truck or an unusually loud noise makes them flair. By late October there are so many ducks at one time taking to the air that our house actually shakes from the wingbeats violently flailing the air as they rise as one. Observing masses of ducks in the air is a thrilling sight. For me, the highlight of any duck-hunting season is that period of two to three hours before the season legally opens. Usually, I'm in my shooting location early and have nothing to do but watch thousands of mallards, teal, wood ducks and bluebills mill around as they're disturbed by other hunters gaining their positions.

One year a lone mallard was flying south and watching me as he flew over my boat. Suddenly he was in the midst of a flock of mallards flying north and actually collided with one in the air. He finally made it through the traffic but was subjected to dirty looks and sharp quacking from the others.

With lots of close-in flying ducks filling the air before opening, it gives me a fine opportunity to watch their flight patterns and to observe just how a duck flies.

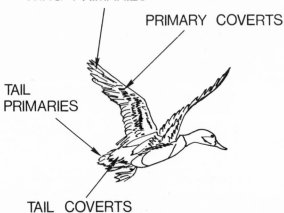

WING PRIMARIES

PRIMARY COVERTS

TAIL PRIMARIES

TAIL COVERTS

Birds have feathers here and there, and on ducks, the feathers at the ends of the wings and tail are the main ones used for flying. These stiff feathers are called the primaries and are in turn partially covered by other feathers called the primary coverts. The primaries are reasonably stiff and can be manipulated by the duck to change the position of the feathers in relation to what the duck is doing at any one time during flight.

PRIMARIES CLOSED

STARTING
THE BEAT

HALF–WAY
FORWARD

How a duck flies

During normal flight, the wing primaries actually act like a propeller on an airplane to pull the duck forward in a screwing action, while the wing itself is thrusting forward and the wing shape is creating a lift to the duck just like in an airplane wing.

The four positions of flight in the pictures help to see what happens during a single wing stroke. Going from the starting to full stroke, the wing primaries are closed and the tips are moved in a screwing motion. On the back stroke, the wing primaries are open to let the air slide through with the least resistance, but even then, the tips are screwed to provide a little further forward motion during the back stroke.

While sitting in my duck boat Saturday afternoon, I had a perfect chance to see the wing tips in action. A big drake mallard came towards me nice and low, just cruising along thinking of a crop full of wild rice when he suddenly spotted me and swung into action. His body went up, his neck went out, and the powerful wings bit into the wind as he rocketed upwards. The wing tips were beautiful and the way they curved around and back as he applied full power made me forget the gun; it was with deep pleasure that I watched him scramble out of range and maybe on to somebody else's hunting spot.

An Indian guide in Canada several years ago taught me that when a duck like a mallard is rising from the water,

PRIMARIES OPEN

FULL   BEAT

HALF—WAY
RETURNING

he can be knocked down from great distances because every feather is fluffed to provide maximum lift during take-off. A short time after telling me this, I was jump-shooting and a greenhead rose up. I shot him and then I measured the distance. The lack of feather protection of the body during the take-off made it possible for me to get him at a distance of 70 yards with number 6 shot from my 12-gauge.

Birds are creatures of beauty with their grace, structure, colors, and habits. I suppose it's because we have more chances to observe the ducks that makes their flight and other habits especially pleasing. It's certainly more fun to watch them fly in their various patterns while duck-hunting than it is to shoot them — but then that's before one comes in range!!

October, 1969

"...Peter Miller Gideon and his wife, Wealthy, arrived in Minnesota from Ohio and settled on the shores of Lake Minnetonka. "

A WEALTH OF APPLES

I made one of my frequent stops at Broms roadside market on Highway 7 as I was going home the other evening, to pick up corn for dinner and muskmelon for breakfast. A stack of beautiful apples caught my eye and a sign proclaimed "Beacon apples." Upon asking, I learned that Beacons were the first of our apples to come on the market each year but it wouldn't be long before the Wealthys came. Just the saying of the name "Wealthy" brought a smile to the face of the salesman.

After leaving the stand, I remembered an historical marker near Excelsior just across County Road 19 near the NSP Service Center and just north of the Minnetonka Country Club. It so happened that my Polaroid camera was in the car, the sun was glinting just right on the metal marker — and as a result you can read all about Peter Gideon and his Wealthy apple (see page 275).

I have since bought some of those first Wealthys of the season and there's no doubt that the variety is the best. A poll of the secretaries in my office placed Wealthys first in preference, followed by Jonathans and then Red Delicious.

A Wealthy apple is described as "Medium size, brilliant red. Good for cold climates. Fruit mildly acid, good quality. Good general purpose apple and especially good for cooking."

The Wealthys that I picked up were still quite green with about 20 percent of the apple a nice red with soft-white freckles and some red streaks mixed in with the dominant green. Eating one was a real treat, so cold, crisp, and crackly. And I liberally dash salt on the firm white meat or flesh before snapping off the next mouthful. (I keep a shaker of salt in my car for this purpose, whenever the spirit moves me.)

"An apple a day keeps the doctor away." There is some truth to that because of the pectin in the apple, a chemical that not only is an aid to digestion but also serves as a solidifying agent when making jams and jellies.

Apples are members of the rose family Rosaceae and have their own genus Malus. The next time you spot a wild rose blooming, check the single blossom and see how similar it is to an apple blossom. Also, the "apple" of a rose gone to seed is like a miniature apple. As a matter of fact, most of our crabapples are developments of wild apples that are just one step away from wild roses.

Supposedly, the first apples came to America from England and were brought by John Endicott in 1629. The apple was widely planted and a John Chapman — "Johnny Appleseed" — spread seeds and plants far and wide across the country. It didn't take long to discover that apples grow best in northern climates and are one of the few fruits that can be grown far north because of their late blossoming, which helps them to escape the normal early frosts.

There are 10,000 varieties of apples in the world and America has about 7,000 of them. However, 18 of these deliver about 90 percent of the commercial crop. Minnesota is not a member of the top 10 state growers. The state of Washington is first, followed by New York. I've driven through upstate New York in the fall and the displays of apples for sale along the roadsides is a beautiful sight.

Technically, the fruit of the apple tree is called a pome and is actually made up of five compartments fused together into a solid mass. Note that the end opposite the stem has five dried little "leaves," vestiges of the five compartments. Also note that the core with the seeds is made up of five divisions.

The historical marker

An apple tree can be started by planting a seed, but apples are peculiar. A tree started from seed will bear fruit much smaller than the original fruit. So most trees are started by "budding," a form of grafting.

Peter Gideon lucked out. That seed from Maine which he planted happened to sire a tree that bore fruit far superior to the original. It occurs that way once in a while. Aren't we lucky he was lucky? I'm also glad his wife was named "Wealthy." I can't imagine biting into a crisp Hildegarde, Gwendolyn, Melba, or Olive.

September, 1970

WATER CLOWNS

Darwin wrote about the survival of the fittest, became
famous for his Origin of the Species theory, and his concepts have been proved so many times they can be regarded
as rules. There is an old saying, however, that there is an
exception that proves the rule — and I vote for the American Coot as the exception that proves the rule of the survival of the fittest.

If there was ever a species that couldn't survive, it's the
coot. He doesn't seem intelligent, he's slow, he's a poor flyer,
he is certainly not attractive looking, and more often than
not he just gets in the way during the duck-hunting season.
I say they're not attractive. I'll take that back. From the
numbers of them, there must be a great attraction between
coots of the opposite sex, at least.

Although the coot or mud hen or rice hen is listed in the
official hunting regulations and is regarded by many as a
duck, it isn't. It's a member of the Rallidae family which
includes the rails and gallinules and is a part of the larger
order Gruiformes that also takes in the cranes. The American Coot has a scientific name of *Fulica americana* and is
really much more like a chicken than a duck. He is the only
sort-of-a-duck-like bird with a distinctive white bill. The
young ones are a downy black with an orange-red head,
but as the season wears on, their body and head turn a slate

gray. In the water, it's almost impossible to mistake a coot because it babbles constantly and pumps its head up and down while swimming.

A coot is a laughable bird. As one author said, "I recommend the funny coot as an antidote for the blues." I've observed them for years, have chased them by boat, have had them come clucking by my duck boat, and many a time a coot on the fly has almost knocked my hat off and my gun down. They babble and they cluck. One person records their voice as "coughing sounds, froglike plunks and a rough sawing or filing as if the saw were stuck — a grating kuk-kuk-kuk-kuk-kuk-kuk."

Each spring and fall we have hundreds if not thousands of coots who spend a few weeks on Lake Minnetonka. A black raft of 35 birds arrived at the Pass Friday, and by Monday morning the group had grown to over 100. Each fall Smiths Bay in the Lower Lake is covered with hundreds and hundreds of coot, dipping and diving for weeds that make up most of their diet. The one attribute they have is their expert diving in deep water. While feeding, they seem to arch their necks and lift their bodies slightly before plunging for a delicious weed, bobbing to the surface like an apple in a tub of water, with a strand that is just as likely grabbed from their mouth by a less ambitious coot. The weed pieces seem to be about six inches long, and I've seen one coot make as many as 50 dives while eating at one "sitting." Imagine the amount of weeds consumed by a flock of 100 birds during one feeding — at least 2,500 feet of weeds.

To watch a coot trying to take off from the water is a sight indeed. He reminds me of a lumbering jet going and going and going before finally lifting off, even though he weighs only one and one-fourth pounds. The coot really works at it. He heads in the general direction that he wants to go, pats the water hard with his feet, beats the water with his wings, and stirs up such a commotion to the water surface that several hundred coot taking off can make a lake look like it's boiling. After flying a short way you can just see him finally say, "Oh the heck with it," and then just collapse

American Coot Taking Off

into the water. How they manage to fly the great distances during migration is a mystery. Also, I've never knowingly seen a flock of coot truly under way and traveling from here to there. Most of the time they're short-range flyers.

If you happen to shoot one by mistake, you'll know it's a coot by the greenish legs, but especially by the fact that its feet have no webs like a duck but rather lobes or scallops on the toes which serve as miniature little paddles. When flying, the coot dangles its legs and they look loose and floppy.

The hunting season for coot is generally the same as for ducks. The limits are usually 15 per day and 30 in possession. The Indian guides in Canada love coot and ask for them as a parting gift. Some American hunters eat them and my neighbor down the shore has the following recipe for them:

Kook-a-Coot a la Creme

Cut away all but the breasts.

Soak breasts in strong soda and water solution for 12 hours or overnight.

Pat dry.

Roll in seasoned flour.

Brown pieces in 1/2 cup hot fat in dutch oven.

Cover with 2 cups sliced onions.

Pour 1 cup milk or cream over all.

Cover tightly and bake 2 hours or until tender at 325 degrees.

Unless you want to go to a lot of trouble to cook them, let them pass by while you're hunting. I think it's a lot more fun to watch their crazy antics than it is to shoot them.

September, 1970

"At Lake of the Woods I have seen...the water
look more like green paint than lake-water and
at Lake Minnetonka...cottagers...complain of
the abundance (of water plant life)...." From
Minnesota Plant Life, Conway McMillan, 1899

THE GOOD OLD DAYS?

During the past couple of years, I have given innumerable speeches on behalf of the Freshwater Biological Institute about our water problems, history of our lakes, and fish studies. As part of my props, I have three bottles — two of them filled with green liquid and one with a white substance. The white water sample is a preserved specimen of an animal bloom that occurred in Minnetonka last year. One of the green bottles holds water from a Minnetonka bay in full bloom. The other green bottle contains water with an algae bloom that I brought back from Lake of the Woods last year. The purpose of these three bottles is to prove that water blooms can be caused by animals as well as algae and that algae blooms can be caused by nature just as much as by man.

I have just returned from this year's week-long hunting and fishing trip to Canada, spent aboard a luxurious houseboat that leaves from Morson, Ontario. Seven wonderful days are spent on Lake of the Woods with its 15,000 islands, far away from most of man, from towns, from sewage effluent, street salts, and farm land run-off.

Without qualification — and I am backed up by the other members of our party (all of whom live on Minnetonka) — the waters of the great Lake of the Woods were once again chock full of a severe bloom of the alga Aphanizomenon flos-aquae, an alga bloom so extensive we have never seen the likes of it on our Lake Minnetonka. The bow wake of an outboard is a solid green blanket, the shore rocks are painted bright blue from dead algae, and waving streaks of special concentrations of the algae, form patterns over the open reaches of water. How a walleye is able to see the bait is a mystery. Most of the time, the secchi disk reading of the turbidity of the water would register about three inches or less.

All of this is a bloom caused by nature, a bloom in a lake that you would think was still clean and pure and relatively untouched by man. The lake is all of these things, but something causes these blooms each fall — and occasionally during the summer. A stranger wouldn't give 2 cents for shoreline property unless the situation was understood.

Do we know what causes blooms like this in a relatively untouched lake? No. I discussed the problem with the houseboat captain, a marvelously huge man with a first-class captain's license obtained while piloting tug boats. His mother was a full-blooded Chippewa Indian who married a full-blooded German from Hanover, Germany during the old logging days. Captain Willie remembers the lake being green off and on ever since the drought of the '30s and theorizes that great bottom areas of the lake became exposed to the air when the lake level dropped over seven feet and somehow or another different conditions prevailed after the level returned to normal. He was born in Morson, Ontario, and was a teenager during the drought, so he should know.

However, the following is an excerpt from a magazine article:

"At Lake of the Woods I have seen...the water look more like green paint than lake-water and at Lake Minnetonka... cottagers...complain of the abundance (of water plant life) ...." From Minnesota Plant Life, Conway McMillan.

The date of this publication was 1899.

Were the good old days always clean and perfect elsewhere? No. Our Minnetonka history is a case in point. It is a well-known fact that around the turn of the century,

Original Lafayette Hotel in 1890s with Great Northern Railway passenger train. From Minnetonka Historical Collection of S. D. Dimond, courtesy of William Lahiff, First National Bank of Navarre, Orono, Minnesota.

several hundred thousand people visited our Lake Minnetonka each year and magnificent steamboats holding up to 2,500 people each plied the waters. But there are records of weed-clogged bays, waters so green there was no swimming, and I'll bet the bacterial coliform count at the shore of those big hotels was something you didn't want to know about. Evidence shows the lake took a drastic turn for the worse in 1870 when the major clearing of land around the lake occurred.

I well remember my mother refusing to let me swim in Lake Harriet in Minneapolis during August — and this was in the 1920s. I well remember the waters of Farm Island Lake north of Lake Mille Lacs in north central Minnesota being green and smelly — and this was in the 1930s. I well remember the waters of Lake Minnetonka and the algae blooms that occurred when we first spent our summers on the lake — and this was in the 1940s.

I guess the point I'm trying to make is that we must be careful to evaluate our present-day water problems with a proper perspective into the past. Too many people remember our waters as having been always crystal-clear and this isn't true. We have problems today that are most serious, but these problems have been caused by nature as well as man. We must understand the causes and find the antidotes.

Green water has been with us in the past, is certainly with us today, and I'm sorry to say will continue to be with us in the future. What we should strike for is a stabilization of our water quality and be willing to settle for our waters hopefully remaining essentially as they are today. That would be a major victory.

October, 1970

SHELLING AT MINNETONKA

A popular pastime for some people is to go shelling along the shores of the ocean, picking up varieties of sea shells and keeping them for aquariums, paperweights, or serious collections. One of the nicest of such collections I've seen was done by Mrs. Ike Clothier of the Philadelphia department store family. She had the shells on display in her home on the shore of magnificent Pageant Beach on Grand Cayman Island in the Caribbean. I've picked up my share of shells, especially during World War II during liberties on countless South Pacific islands.

Over the past many years at the Pass on Minnetonka, I've been shelling on our shore — but for a different kind of shell. I have been told that the Pass was once one of the best duck-hunting spots in the state, and I believe it because of the number of old shotgun shells that keep working up out of the sand for me to pick up and keep.

The other day I decided it was time for me to know more about these old shells, so I made a date with Ozzie Klavestad at the Stagecoach Museum east of Shakopee and spent a delightful late afternoon with him. His collection of guns and shells is the finest in the country and I couldn't have talked with a better person to give me the history of these old shells.

All that remained of those that I had picked up were

the brass ends with particles of paper wadding still attached. Without exception, the brass shell bases from the shores of Minnetonka were pre-World War I and most of them were probably shot between 1900 and 1910. Ozzie could tell this because (1) the use of smokeless powder in shotgun shells didn't start until 1896 and these were bases from smokeless shells; and (2) the primer pins were small, an irregularity used with smokeless powder until larger primer pins were used starting in 1910.

Even today, shotgun shells are classified, in general, as low-base and high-base, which means that the brass portion of the shells is low (maybe a half-inch long) or high (as much as one and a half inches long). The more powerful the shell, the higher the base which serves as a "backstop" or container of the force when the shell is fired. Every action has an opposite and equal reaction, and the brass bases help control the action and reaction within the shell.

Some of the shells I found were low-base and assumed to be trap-shooting loads used by someone for duck hunting. One shell was a 12-gauge U.M.C. Co. Nitro-Club, manufactured by the Union Metallic Cartridge Co., a company purchased some time ago by the Remington Arms Co. Other low-base shells were Western Field 12- and 16-gauge, which were popular trap shells sold by Sears Roebuck and other hardware store chains like Marshall Wells of the old days. All of these low-base shells still have some of the paper of the shell body preserved within the brass case.

The high-base shells that I collected are all 12-gauge and of only two brands, Winchester Leader and Western Record. The latter shells appear to have come from the same gun because of a peculiar marking on the shell end by the firing pin of the gun.

Ozzie Klavestad told me many interesting things about shotguns and their shells. For instance, the term "12-gauge" means nothing today except as a reference to a size of shell which we've become used to. The original 12-gauge shell was made in England and the terminology defined the shell as having steel balls of a size that weighed 12 to the pound. Ten-gauge had 10 to the pound, 20-gauge 20 to the pound.

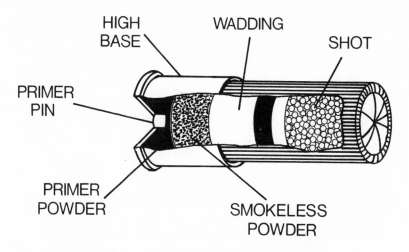

HIGH BASE

WADDING

SHOT

PRIMER PIN

PRIMER POWDER

SMOKELESS POWDER

TYPICAL SHOTGUN SHELL

Over the years, shotguns have been made to handle shells as large as 2-gauge and as small as 9mm for taxidermist use. Gauges usually go by even numbers so there have been 2, 4, 8, 10, 14, 16, 20 and 28 gauges. The 2, 4, and 8 gauges are now illegal, but were used by market hunters who could kill 50 ducks at a time, using guns such as a double 4-gauge that weighed 24 pounds.

The .410 shotgun uses shells that measure less than a half-inch in diameter (four hundred and ten thousandths of an inch) and this size of shell two inches long was first used by taxidermists in Europe. Americans picked it up as a sporting gun, made 2½-inch shells for a while, and today the 3-inch .410 shell is common. I was recently told of a duck hunter who used a .410 and killed 15 out of 17 ducks. I shoot a .410 but only for partridge and maybe pheasants if they're holding tight.

Of the many special shotguns that Ozzie showed me from the Stagecoach Museum was a serial number 1 Model 97 Winchester, the first repeating shotgun made by Winchester in 1897 (I owned a Model 97 for many years). He also let me handle and sight the beautiful repeating shotgun made around 1905 that was the favorite gun used by Annie Oakley in her marksmanship act. I asked him whether he ever saw her act and Ozzie said no, but at the age of 11 he did sit on the lap of Buffalo Bill.

Shotgun shells have been made out of most any material and for many a use. Ozzie gave me two special shells to keep. One was a German shell that contained a wicked looking slug instead of small shot; the other was a 10-gauge shell made by R. F. (whoever that is) and the paper end of the shell is marked "Very M.K. 11 white signal light," a flare, I guess.

Ozzie says that locally-made Federal shells came up with one of the most important contributions to the art of shotgun shells by designing a special wadding that prevented "lateral shots" or shot patterns that strayed from the direction of aiming. I've always liked Federals and have used them for nearly thirty-five years.

I still search the shores for old shell bases, especially after strong east winds have churned the sands. The hunters may be gone, but the shells and ducks remain. It's fun and interesting to come across bits of history like this.

October, 1970

*"...we became suspended between two huge
waves...and for a period of seconds...the entire
ship...would bounce up and down like a
rubber ball."*

THE WAY OF A WAVE

After it was all over, I knew that I would probably never
again be truly afraid. It was World War II, we were well off
the island of Okinawa (Formosa), we had split off from a
convoy of lighter ships, and we had just finished riding out
a fiendish typhoon. We learned afterwards that destroyers
had rolled over and sunk, ships had broken in two, and I
saw the bow of an aircraft carrier that had been peeled back
a hundred feet, like a fragile egg shell, from the force of
the waves.

I recount this episode because I want to discuss waves —
and I saw waves during that typhoon the likes of which I
never want to see again. Our ship was over 650 feet long
(longer than two football fields), a C4 built by the Kaiser
shipyards and made entirely of steel. Yet time and again
during the typhoon we became suspended between two huge
angry waves, by the bow and the stern of the ship, with
troughs so deep there was no water underneath our mid-
section. The ship would sag in the middle, the hull would
spring back, and for a period of seconds at a time, the entire
ship — and we — would bounce up and down like a rubber
ball. Some ships couldn't take the strain. Ours was new
enough to last and APA234 is forever dear to my heart.

But then, everything is relative and I've experienced some
pretty wild water off the ocean, too. One of those times

happened when riding into the teeth of a high strong steady wind on Lake of the Woods in an outboard, in the dark, with full hunting gear on. We came through, thanks to the skill of our Indian guide.

In my humble opinion, the thing that makes rough water so tough is the awesome power of the waves. When water gets moving, the terrible energy tied up in its motion can't be denied and you either go with it or give up. It gets its way.

To understand waves, there is one simple fact to remember. The motion that you see as a wave travels is not the mass of water moving, but rather, the force that caused the wave traveling from water particle to water particle. The traveling wave is the form this transferred energy has taken. Water is made up of molecules. Any outside force can cause these molecules to move. Drop a stone in the water, have a boat go by, have the wind blow across the surface of the water, and energy is imparted to the water molecules. This energy causes one molecule to move, he bumps his neighbor — and so on and so on. To prove that the water itself does not move as a wave passes, try the classic test of throwing a cork onto the water. A wave will come, the cork will rise and fall — but will stay right where it was while the wave continues on.

Our common type of wave is a surface wave that has a circling type of motion. This is caused by the outside source of energy raising a water molecule and then the force of

ENERGY IN WATER TRAVELS LEFT TO RIGHT.

gravity lowers the molecule. This up and down force, coupled with the directional force like a wind blowing from the west, causes the cycloid pattern of energy to travel with the wind.

Waves are caused by three major events (ignoring boats and such): the wind, earthquakes, and the gravitational pull of the sun and the moon. We haven't had any earthquakes lately and Minnetonka is too small to be affected noticeably by the moon and sun, so our waves are the results primarily of winds.

Wind waves and their sizes and shapes are affected by three factors: the velocity or strength of the wind, the distance that the wind has a chance to blow across open water, and the length of time the wind doth blow. As a wave develops, it has a crest and a trough. The extent of its wave length and its wave height depends upon the severity of the wind factors. In 1933, a Navy ship en route from Manila to California accurately measured a wave 112 feet high caused by a storm that covered thousands of miles at sea. This wave had the velocity, distance, and time to become a record wave.

Whitecaps are the tips of waves that are blown off by the wind and are actual water. Breakers along a shore or in shallow water are caused by the shallowness interrupting the cycloid pattern of the wave and the crest breaks, throwing actual water forward. If you ever want to build a breakwater

FLOAT TRAVELS IN CIRCLE BUT STAYS
IN SAME RELATIVE POSITION.

for protection, build the breakwater in water too deep to break. Waves not breaking have little destructive force against a wall as their force is a rolling type. Breaking waves are murder and just don't try to fight them.

The study of waves has been a true science and all is not known about them yet. But I've learned to respect them and to understand them. Believe me, they're much larger than you are.

October, 1970

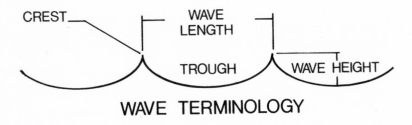

WAVE TERMINOLOGY

*"...in 1905...there was green water then and
there's some now....the weeds and the reeds
are in the same spots...."*

BACK WHEN

Many has been the time I've stood on our deck overlooking
the lake, romanticizing about the past. Visions danced before my eyes of Indians roaming the big woods, lake waters
so clear you located your fish before dropping the hook, and
shorelines untouched, with giant trees reaching to the very
water's edge. How long ago were things like that? Fifty
years? One hundred and fifty years?

Last weekend, I listened to Lester tell me facts of sixty-five
years ago on a large lake in northern Minnesota. I was im-
pressed because some of the things he told me I wouldn't
have guessed.

Lester was born those sixty-five years ago, in 1905, not
two miles away from where he was now sitting in front of
a huge fireplace, drinking the logger's drink of vodka and
water without ice. As the flames flickered, they played on
his white shock of hair and accentuated the somewhat heavy
build of his body. Between gulps (they drink their drinks,
man, none of this sipping stuff), he deftly shifted a toothpick
around his mouth with his tongue while he talked of the
days that were.

How are the lakes today compared with their conditions
dozens of years ago? Lake levels are about the same — down
a bit during the drought in the '30s (only two feet down) —
but today close to the levels he knew as a boy. Water quality

is the same. There was some green water then and there's some now. He recalls the weeds and the reeds are in the same spots and no heavier or lighter in growth. There are more boats and motors, but that is due to the development of the outboard.

There are fewer people up there now than in years past. The woods are heavier and taller than when he was a boy. There are more roads through the woods here and there and, as a consequence, there are more hunters and less game, but the type of game hasn't changed. Within his memory, moose weren't around even though his lake was named after the animal. Partridge numbers have declined over the years; he claims he once shot a partridge with a slingshot.

The most surprising statement Lester made was that, when he was a boy, his family laid in provisions for the summer — not the winter. Back in those days there were no automobiles and the Great Northern Railroad from Duluth reached only to Deer River, many miles to the south of his house. Their route to town was across the ice from lake to lake and over frozen, small logging roads, so it was possible to get to town in the wintertime, but it was too hard in the summer. Barrels of salt pork, sacks of flour, salt, sugar, spices, and all things nice were brought in for the summer. It was then they had nothing to do and passed the time hunting, fishing, and playing around.

He guessed it was around 1920 that Thorpe Bros. from Minneapolis bought up whole stretches of shorelines and developed the area. One section was called Oklahoma Hill because a deer hunter from that southerly state loved the north woods, went home, and passed the word. The result was that a colony from the south made annual visits to their summer places way up north. Today only one person of the original group remains — an old lady who lives alone.

I'd like to hunt with Lester sometime. He recently returned from Vandalia, Ohio, where the Grand American Trap Shoot is held each year. One day he shot at and broke 97 out of 100 and 99 out of 100. The champion broke 500 straight targets over a four-day period. Les was in charge

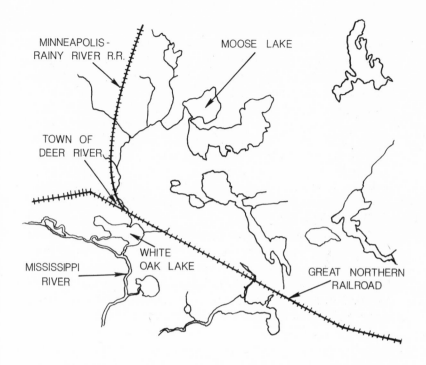

Deer River, Minnesota, was a logging "crossroads" for the M & R
and Great Northern Railroads around 1900. Logs were brought by
rail and unloaded into White Oak Lake, which is connected with
the Mississippi River. From there the logs were floated to lumber
mills at Minneapolis. There were no established roads in the area
so area residents traveled in the wintertime when the lakes were
frozen, remaining "home" in the summers. A recent area history
published by the Deer River Federated Women's Club states,
"During these years the deer limit was three to a hunter, and at
the height of the season the M & R would bring down 350 deer
every other day. I can remember how we used to run from school
to see the frozen deer piled like cordwood on the depot platform."

of several trap ranges during the shoot and said the noise from sunrise to sunset was like a dozen firecracker strings going off constantly. Imagine 3,000 shooters in one day firing from 48 ranges in the main line and seven practice ranges on the side.

What about the future? Les and his wife want to live in northern Minnesota, where they are, as long as they can. They go south once in a while during the winters, and off and on his wife cooks for a hunting lodge in Florida. Within a week, Les hopes to go to the Montana-Wyoming border area to shoot ducks and geese "where they still fly like in the good old days."

From the way these two people hurry around in their red Volkswagon, haul the wood, light the fires, cook with huge appetites waiting, and still remain smiling and relaxed, I'll bet they're around for a good long time. I'm already looking forward to next year and another good talk. I'll also bring a more liberal supply of vodka with me.

November, 1970

*"She was something precious and
should never be forgotten."*

MY LADY OF THE LAKE

On election day, I voted twice. The first time was for the candidates of my choice. The second time I had no choice. I told the doctor at the animal hospital to put my old friend away.

It will be thirteen years this next Easter Sunday when Sandra joined our family, and well I remember that day. Our three boys each had a yellow Easter duckling paddling around in a wash tub in our den while I looked in the Sunday paper want ads for a possible dog. We answered an ad and drove to north Minneapolis to find Sandra for sale, tied up in a back yard, thin and spooky and not at all the way a six-month-old golden retriever should be. She had faith and came with us.

As my wife said recently, "She was something precious and should never be forgotten." That Sandra was. Now, I know a dog is only a dog, but once in a while a super one comes along. This one was without a doubt the smartest, nicest animal with a delightful sense of humor and a special feeling for Minnetonka, near which she spent most of her life.

Many has been the time we cruised the lake with our two goldens on the rear seat, younger Molly sniffing the air and watching the other boats and people lining the channels, while Sandra relaxed on the cushion, at ease with the sounds of the waves, the vibration of the engine, and our voices remarking about the beautiful sights. A favorite pastime of Sandra's was to stand belly-deep in the lake shallows and watch the sunfish swim around and feel them peck at her legs. One day she caught a weakened sunfish and for days she strutted around as if it had been a record sailfish.

Have you ever had a dog — or any animal for that matter — who not only loved artichokes but knew how to eat them? Sandra preferred less lemon and more butter, thank you — but she properly bared her teeth and would scrape the goodness of the leaf without her teeth so much as touching the leaf. She really would eat anything, but would touch nothing if I told her not to. My garden is strictly off limits to the dogs, but Sandra enjoyed the fall work of pulling up the garden when she could enter and eat all the tomatoes she wanted. Yellow kumquats were of particular delight to her and she would go through several dozen at a time.

Sandra was a regal lady. People who didn't know her well would call her Sandy, but you notice I called her nothing but Sandra. She was a great smiler and each evening would greet me with a big grin on my arrival home. If she knew she did something a little wrong — like spilling water out of the bird bath while taking a drink — she would smile and smile and smile for hours every time I looked at her.

Although never professionally trained, she was a great huntress and behaved perfectly in the field. Her first brush with a pheasant occurred when she was taking a drink alongside a pond and a cock burst from the grass right next to her. She went one way and the pheasant went the other. Since that time, I think Sandra tried especially hard while hunting pheasants, and a sliced nose and cut footpads from dried stalks and grass were all part of the game.

Of all food, popcorn was her first love. Without popcorn I don't think the Gray family would survive. As we munched, we'd toss bits to Sandra and Molly and, over the years, Sandra became the Brooks Robinson of the popcorn circuit. During her final year, I had to have good aim as her eyesight failed, but her timing was still there.

How do you say good-bye to a supposedly dumb animal?

Sandra

How do you adequately thank something for years of enjoyment? I'll never forget her patience while the kids bandaged her during a doctor game, or her stance on the dock watching the crappies and sunfish laze away the hot day beneath the boat canopy, or her love of music and hot fires in the den on a cold night, or her delight in tennis games as she lay on the grass outside the gate to greet us all between sets, or her soft mouth that could carry anything without a tooth mark, or her acceptance of other dogs or ducks or cats or little children if she was asked to do so.

She was a dog with a fine sense for living. Her left and right paw shakes, her soft and loud barks, her reactions to situations without being told what to do made her a respected member of our family — a real lady of our beloved lake.

My last shake of that old gray muzzle was a hard thing to do, but I don't think she saw or heard me. As I walked away from that building with young dogs barking, I reminded myself that grown men don't cry. It just looks like they do sometimes.

How much will Sandra be missed? Let's quote a few lines from T. L. Beddoes:

> Tell me how many beads there are
> In a silver chain
> Of an evening rain.

November, 1970

*"...the initial white lump...was caused by a shot
of formic acid; the prolonged swelling was
caused by a histamine substance...."*

BEE, WHERE IS THY STINGER?

Sunday morning, one of my sons came limping into the house
with an enlarged ankle that seemed to spill out over the top
of his tennis shoe. He was moaning and groaning about this
bee that somehow or other had crawled into his shoe the day
before, become lodged under the tongue and, in self defense,
stung him fair and square.

Almost immediately, a hard, white circle formed around
the bite and after the initial hurt, it itched and gradually the
bump went down and finally disappeared. But an hour or two
after that, the ankle started to swell to proportions of un-
comfortableness, and for at least forty-eight hours, the foot
remained enlarged until it slowly worked its way back to
normal.

Five things can be said of this experience: The bee was a
worker honey bee; the bee didn't want to sting him; the
initial white lump was caused by a shot of formic acid; the
prolonged swelling was caused by a histamine substance that
was part of the bee's venom; and, my son is lucky that he
does not have a super-sensitivity to the bite of a bee.

Bees are nice and without them we'd be in sad shape.
The delicious honey that they produce is beside the point;
their great contribution to the world is the pollination that
results from their visiting one bloom after another in search
for nectar. In the process, they haul specks of pollen on

their body hairs from flower to flower, causing our myriads of fruits and seeds to develop from the flowers.

The common type of honey bee is a social creature and a particular hive or group is made up of three types of bees: the queen, the drones, and the workers. Drones can't bite as they have no stinger; queens rarely sting anything other than other young queens; therefore, it probably was a worker honey bee that did the stinging of my son.

As the drawings show, the stinger of a queen is smooth and she can repeatedly sting, whereas the stinger of a worker bee is barbed and as it stings, the stinger becomes caught in the victim, a chunk of the bee's abdomen is torn away when it leaves, and the bee dies. The stingers are usually about one third the length of the bee's body. They're hollow and the stinging fluid from the bee is pumped through the stinger into the victim.

Bees are usually gentle creatures and a worker bee will sting only when the hive is in danger or when in trouble away from the hive, such as being caught under the tongue of a shoe.

Part of the sting of a bee is caused by formic acid shot into the skin of the victim. This acid has the formula $HCOOH$ and is a member of the organic carboxyl group with the -COOH component. It is found in bees, wasps, stinging nettles, hornets, red ants, and in the needles of some fir trees. The liquid is colorless, has a sharp smell, and in industry is used to coagulate and precipitate gold, silver, mercury and pure rubber from liquid latex. Formic acid neutralizers include ammonia, bluing, onion juice, and baking soda. It apparently is the formic acid that causes the initial "blow" and white lump of a bee sting.

The venom inserted by the bee while stinging has a very serious side to it, however, apart from the initial formic acid reaction. Along with the acid, small amounts of a deadly liquid containing histamine-like substances are present. For a person who is highly sensitive to such chemicals, one or more bee, wasp, or hornet bites can result in bad trouble. These histamine-like chemicals have a formula similar to regular histamine, which is $C_5H_9N_3$, found in ergot (a fungus

302

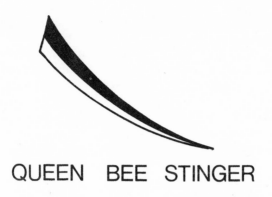

QUEEN BEE STINGER

WORKER BEE STINGER

growth), and affects the blood vessels through very severe dilation. In some people, this rapid swelling can be throughout the body, even closing off the throat. Also, very sensitive people find the chemicals destructive to the nervous system, and a very toxic protein in the venom can cause blood cells to be destroyed with the resultant violent reactions.

According to a doctor friend of mine, highly sensitive people can be desensitized by taking a series of twenty or more shots. If a sensitive person is bitten and a violent reaction results, adrenaline is the immediate thing to use as it works faster than a normal anti-histamine drug.

Obviously, a doctor should also be called immediately.

A normal person can survive from 500 to 1,000 bee stings (heaven forbid!!) but for those special cases where one bite can be terribly serious, adrenaline should be kept on hand. I know of some people who carry some with them all the time.

So, the moral to this whole business with bees is to like them, to respect them, but don't dilly-dally with a bite if you or somebody you know can be highly sensitive to them. Bees and bee stings are fairly common this time of year. Let's hope your experience with bees is limited to enjoying their honey.

September, 1971

*"Politicians...have pondered why Minnesota
turns out the breed of person it does —
dynamic, on the liberal side, concerned
with people."*

A TIME FOR CHANGE

A friend of mine sent me a clipping from the Los Angeles
Times dated September 30. The theme of the article by
Jack Smith was that Californians don't miss the changing
of seasons because such changes are the very things that
triggered people to move to the southwest. He didn't mention the fact that people are now moving east from California and for the first time in recent history, more people
leave than come to California. Be that as it may, Smith
ended his editorial with this anecdote: It was dark when
his wife came home and he said to her, "It seems like fall
already," and she said, "Yes, fall was last Thursday," and
he said, "How did you know that?" and she said, "I read it.
It was in the paper."

Thank goodness we don't have to read about it to know
that fall is here and how beautiful it is. Along with spring,
summer, and winter, I think fall is the nicest time of the year.

The vegetable garden is coasting downwards to the hard
freeze that is bound to come one of these nights. The
tomatoes are on the small side, the cucumbers short and
pudgy, and the acorn squash leaves are limp and sparse,
exposing the dark green fruits that are so delicious when
baked with butter and brown sugar.

Lake temperatures are heading for the lower degrees and
just about now the lake is very unstable and should be

turning over with fresh dissolved oxygen replenishing the deeps. For the next couple of weeks, bits of weeds, and some discoloration of the water, will give evidence of the water turnover.

Politicians the country over have pondered why Minnesota turns out the breed of person it does — dynamic, on the liberal side, concerned with people. Industrialists have long known that the skills of Minnesotans rank with the country's best. We historically have had the lowest of Army physical rejections. An eastern friend of mine located here because of the high rate of invention of devices, and the formation of corporations with great potential.

I don't necessarily mean to be blowing our own horn, except maybe to make the point that all of these attributes of Minnesota people could be a result of the changes that occur with the seasons. Everything changes constantly and when you're more aware of change, then change is second nature to you. You live with change, you adapt to change, you think change. I hope such change doesn't change.

Unless we stand back and think about it, so much of change happens without our realizing it. Take Minnesota football. It wasn't so many years ago that the Gophers were top dog in fall interest in our area but yet, suddenly, attendance at games is limping along in the 30 thousands and the University is losing money with a single program that used to support the whole athletic program. Take Attica and the sweeping prison reforms that are bound to come because of the killings, a tragic happening caused by the need for changes unrecognized until too late. Take war and welfare, the condition of the dollar, the cost of building and high taxes that in combination are bringing a new way of living for Americans — the end of the single-family unit?

Another change is happening the country over, one of which most people are unaware, and that is a change in the attitudes of some of the major companies and the executives who run them. I was indeed fortunate to be a part of a fifty-man team that recently spent a solid week examining the pros and cons of what we are, have been, and are apt to be. At the location of the seminar, the foliage was just starting

THE DIFFERENCE IS
THE FLICK OF A SWITCH

OFF   ON

An example of what the new industrial man can do

to change at the beginning of the week. As the days slipped by, the golds and reds and pinks and yellows deepened and glowed, almost as if their changes were matching the subtle changes occurring in the participants of the study in constant session. The boiling of ideas and the turmoil from challenge going on in the minds of the seminar members were matched by the joy of peaceful walks, stately deer framed against the colors of the woods, and partridge camouflaged amongst the dried leaves and brush.

The net result of this change happening in industry and those associated with it — including governmental, academic and religious men — is that there will be a new type of man concerned with the worker, conditions, the neighborhood, and the environment. The main emphasis will not be on "bottom line" profits, but rather on what the company can contribute to a better life. Money will be returned to the social and natural life much as money has been returned to inner-company research and investments for the sole purpose of making more money.

This net result will be a new industrial man. It will take time, but realize that this type of change is going on although we may not be aware of it because we're living with it on a daily basis. Just like our beautiful fall colors that change each day. Little by little the colors of the past are finally shed, making ready for a new season, a new image, a coat made of new cloth. So with our companies and institutions, a change is underway which is good because it is the time for change.

October, 1971

*"The whole secret is to cover the bushes...
not to keep them from getting too cold,
but to keep them from getting too warm."*

PUTTING ROSES TO BED

At about this same time last year, I wrote about the problem
I have had every year trying to decide how to cover or care
for our roses for the winter. This coming winter will be the
twenty-fifth time we've faced the issue and I'm going to do
what I did last year — dig up the whole rose bush, throw it
into a trench in my vegetable garden, cover it with dirt, pile
some mulched leaves over the trench, and then relax until
next spring.

By following this procedure a year ago, we didn't lose a
rose during the winter and started the spring season with
bushes that had long green stems at the time of replanting.
Every plant was healthy and we have gotten 3 or 4 crops of
big rose blooms through the growing season. I'm satisfied
and sold on the results.

Of course, everybody is on his own and I accept no
responsibility for what you do, but I'm waiting until the
first good hard freeze kills the foliage and the rose leaves
either drop or wilt. Then, about a week or two later, each
of our couple of dozen bushes will be carefully dug up, the
dirt shaken from the roots, and the whole plant laid in a
trench at least a foot deep and wide and long enough to
accommodate the bushes. No part of the plant should be
less than four inches from the surface when covered with
soil, and the leaves are insurance against loss.

The reasons behind this procedure make sense. At a temperature less than 31 degrees, a rose plant is "set," the leaves drop, and the sugars in the upper parts of the plant descend to the roots. The plant goes dormant. In this condition, the whole plant can be disturbed and stored without damage to it, as long as the roots and other parts aren't subjected to varying temperatures during dormancy and especially don't get warm even once during this period. After the whole plant is buried at least four inches under ground and covered with hay or leaves, the risk of the plant being warmed by a winter thaw or hot sun on a mild day is minimal. The plant stays dormant and safe until dug up after thawing in the spring and replanted. This happens any time between April 10 and May 1.

Most amateur rose growers don't follow this system and claim to have good results either heaping dirt over the rose crown and bending the canes down for covering, or piling two or three feet of leaves and hay and what-not over the plants. However, rose bushes too close to a house foundation where some heat leaks out during the winter, or bushes in confined gardens where there isn't room to bend the canes or properly cover the bushes, should be given special care. Trench-burying them is a good way to go.

I discussed the whole matter with a commercial rose grower, a man who depended upon 28,000 rose plants for his livelihood over a period of twenty years. He's what I'd call a pro. He agrees with me that trenching is a most successful way to handle the plants for winter. The whole secret is to cover the bushes with enough protection — not to keep them from getting too cold, but to keep them from getting too warm. An early snow cover is a great help under all circumstances.

Several interesting facts came out of my talk with this rose grower. He has sold as many as 80,000 roses in a five-day period — out of a total of 2,000,000 roses sold in our Twin City area during Valentine's Day time. However, Mother's Day is the number one rose day in our area. The commercial red rose is usually Forever Yours, large and deep red with a good "shelf life." Cara Mia is a new red coming up fast. The usual white rose is White Butterfly, the pinks Corina or Pink Sensation, and the yellows Electra. My friend with one acre of roses under glass said that most commercial roses are now grown in Arizona and California, and that Portland, Oregon, has an ideal climate for roses — cool and mild. This has been a good rose year for our area because of the cool and damp summer.

He suggests that when the rose bushes are replanted in the spring, a balanced soil be used for planting and the plants be well watered. He has used rice hulls in a 20:1 ratio for mixing with the soil. He claims cocoa bean hulls attract rodents when used, but I haven't found that to be true, even though I've used them for several years. I don't know about rice hulls, but cocoa bean hulls can be purchased at local stores.

Further information from my "pro": Ideal growing temperatures for roses are 60 degrees at night and 70 degrees during the day. Hot weather causes the roses to grow too fast, stems are weaker, and flowers are poorer. In our area, roses can have as many as three peak blooming periods, spaced about six weeks apart. Average blooming times are June 20, August 1, and September 15. Bushes should be fertilized every four weeks, about two weeks before the peak blooming time, and the soil should be well wetted when fertilizing. Blooming periods six weeks apart is an average. Some rose varieties take 42 days, some 47 days, and some 54 days from "cut to bloom."

My wife and I have had the fun and joy of a rose garden. Nothing is prettier and more satisfying than a dozen or more rose bushes in full bloom in June, in partial bloom in July and August, and back in full bloom from September until heavy frost. Not only is the rose bed a gorgeous sight with white, pink, yellow, and red blooms, but cut roses last for days in bud vases and other similar tall slim containers.

My favorite "pot" for roses is a delicate tear-drop hanging vase. It's most decorative with a freshly-cut rose and leaf showing a sharp outline against the window. This glass thing caught my eye while I was shopping several years ago in the famous N-K department store in Stockholm, Sweden. It sur-

Tear-drop vase: survivor of travels and storms

vived the trip back to Minneapolis (its neck is only ¼ inch in diameter) and was hanging from the ceiling when the 1965 tornado destroyed our house at the Pass. The tear-drop was found several days later lying in a pine tree quite removed from the house — unbroken and ready for hanging in the new house.

A rose in this tear-drop will always have a special meaning to us.

October, 1971
October, 1972

"They don't hibernate in the true sense...
but rather go into a deep sleep...."

WHERE DO ALL THE CHIPMUNKS GO?

The rise and fall of the yields of plants and the populations of animals have always occurred and will continue to do so. A bumper crop of corn one year, another year hardly any apples, another year too many or too few acorns — and this year, a super-duper supply of chipmunks. I had noticed more of them than usual this summer, but I figured this was because my old golden retriever Sandra had died last fall. She had been most effective in keeping the chipmunk numbers at a reasonable level.

A friend of mine changed my mind about the reason for the quantities around, however. He remarked one day in July that there were so many chipmunks around his property it was necessary to trap some of them. He seemingly still had just as many after he had caught twenty-nine right around his house. Obviously, it was a good chipmunk year, but the why of it is not known. Probably, the type of winter and the ability of large numbers of adults to enter springtime in good breeding shape is the number one why-of-it.

Chipmunks live in a network of passageways in the ground, a number of which I know I have under my lawn and near my house. At odd spots around my yard are holes about one and a half inches in diameter which are entrances to the underground network. Within these passages, chipmunks spend the cold season. They don't hibernate in the true sense of the word, but rather go into a deep sleep when the coldness comes and will awaken, stir around, and eat during mild spells of the winter. As evidence of this, my next door neighbor had observed a chipmunk eating at his bird feeder during the winter and took a colored picture of the thing on the ground when it was below zero. We reasoned the passageways he used were close to the house and therefore warm so the chipmunk was active most of the winter.

I believe chipmunks can go "inactive" as a protective device at almost any time. Three years ago, late in the fall, I was checking my sparrow trap during a cold rainy evening and found a chipmunk in the trap. He was motionless so I picked him up and thought him dead. He was stone cold but his eyes were clear and his body was pliable. I brought him into the house, made a comfortable box with a soft towel in it and placed him near a roaring fire in the fireplace. In an hour or two he was stirring around, was soon eating bits of tomato and drinking water, and at the end of the evening was normal in all respects. He had survived a trapping.

I suppose we've all seen chipmunks loading up their cheek pouches with food. I once caught one with fourteen ground cherries in the pouch — and ground cherries average about one-half inch in diameter. I would guess they can carry twenty-five to thirty kernels of corn, and I have a picture of a bulging chipmunk face with the pouch full of ninety-three ragweed seeds. This food is carried to the passageways and stored for the winter.

The chipmunk, therefore, is a prime example of animals that hibernate to one degree or another. Hibernators live in the north and do not migrate. Almost without exception, they are vegetarians and when the cold weather arrives, their food supply disappears. As a survival device they merely go inactive. Because they become inactive during a severe season, almost all are burrowing animals. They are removed from the elements but near a food supply for an occasional late winter snack. Animals that hibernate to a minor degree are squirrels, bears, skunks, and raccoons.

Eastern Chipmunk

Hunger and a rise in temperature are the two main reasons they stir around in the winter.

There are some animals, however, that hibernate in the true sense and actually undergo physiological changes. Woodchucks and hamsters are examples. Besides sleeping (*hibernus* is Latin for winter sleep), the body temperature, respiration, and the nervous system show a marked change. Blood temperatures may fall as low as the surrounding temperature and at times almost to freezing. Breathing becomes extremely slow, and a woodchuck has been found to breathe as few times as twelve per hour while hibernating. The whole nervous system becomes inactive and these animals will respond only to the strongest kind of stimulus. An animal in this stage must be handled carefully as the body is not ready to cope with great activity.

A deep sleep like hibernation in the wintertime can occur

in the summer, too. It's called estivation, and there are types of snails that become inactive during hot, dry spells.

Last winter we had a fine snow cover and we ended up with a good crop of chipmunks. I predict lots of snow this winter, too — so the chipmunk supply next summer could be a liberal one. I love chipmunks and really hate to weed them out. But they are living with us when they move in under our houses or throughout our lawns, and periodic thinning is a price they have to pay — right or wrong.

November, 1971

THE PRICE OF USAGE

As we were driving home from the airport Tuesday evening, we stopped at a fruit and vegetable stand on Highway 5 east of Chanhassen to pick up some fresh corn for supper. While doing so, a home grown cantaloupe lying on the counter with a price of 50 cents appeared to be a good buy, and I bought it. Then, I noticed that under the counter was a basket full of cantaloupe priced at 10 cents each. A closer look showed that these cheapies were misshapen and partly rotten. For all practical purposes they were not worth even 10 cents as far as I was concerned.

The good one that I bought was worth 50 cents because I could use it. The cheap ones weren't worth anything because I couldn't use them.

Roughly a million new cars are purchased and placed on our highways each year in the United States, and we think nothing of losing at least $600 per year in depreciation on each of these cars. I guess we're willing to drop this amount of money because we are getting a use out of the car that makes the price right.

The point is that we're conditioned to spending money for material things, knowing that as we buy these things they are decreasing through depreciation. We haven't projected this kind of conditioning to those parts of our lives that aren't as factual or as concrete or as material.

317

What price do you put on the right and the opportunity to arrive at Gooseberry Falls on the North Shore and spend a full weekend camping? What cost are we willing to bear to insure a decent environment one, three, or five generations from now?

Our country is basically run by the laws of supply and demand. For instance, the right to own land privately has been fundamental to our lives, but I can visualize the day when no one person can own a piece of land because land will be so precious and in such short supply that the demand will drive the price out of range, taxes will be unbearable, and the land will revert to general public ownership.

Last year I was in New York State deep in harness-racing country attending a very nice party, and during the conversation I made the remark that, in my opinion, it wouldn't be long before it was necessary to have reservations to attend any or all of our public parks. You will have to call in advance and get a number to place your boat in the water of a public lake on a certain day and at a certain hour. I shocked several people at this party with such talk but the time is nearly here (in 1972) when such things are going to be the usual.

For the past two years, it has been necessary to close Yellowstone Park for several days during the height of the tourist season because the park was full and no more cars or people could be taken inside. On the opening weekend of Disney World in Florida in 1971, thousands of people were turned away and an immense traffic jam extended for dozens of miles in all directions. Just recently, I drove to the Maroon Bells, those three beautiful mountain peaks deep in the Colorado Rockies, and found that the road leading to the area was blocked by a National Park Service entrance booth, manned (or ladied?) by a pretty and smiling woman employee. Each car had to state its purpose for passing the gate. Campers had to pay a fee, were assigned a campsite, given instructions on how to behave, advised they had a maximum of three days to stay, and could be fined at a later date if they didn't behave properly or leave the campsite in good shape for the next camper.

An irreversible excessive supply: northern/crappie

And why not? As more and more people have more and more leisure time, our parks and lakes and recreational areas are going to be used more and more. I would rather use something less often but enjoy it more when I do than not enjoy it at all. I would rather take my turn to boat on a lake with a limited number of other boats than try to boat with an unlimited number beyond control.

How to control the number of people using an area is one thing. Keeping the area in usable shape is something else again. Now, we're getting back to the cost of using something, using that intangible thing called the environment. When we use the water for boating and swimming and fishing, when we use the land for camping and hiking and hunting, when we use the air for flying and viewing and living, we must eventually pay for such a privilege.

These factors of our environment are depreciating just the same as that new car of yours is depreciating. The expense is there in the water, land, and air, just like your car. We have to understand this, to be ready to pay for this. It is the price of usage.

We are accustomed to paying a high price for a seat in an airplane. A fare is fair. We are conditioned to paying a lesser price to use a highway through taxes and licenses. We must get used to paying for the right to travel over the waters and across and through the woods.

The law of supply and demand is a relentless thing and sometimes it's hard to figure it out. An example is the price of a ranch deep in the Rockies. Because it is located within fifteen miles of a major ski area, its 500 acres with buildings is priced for sale at a cool $1½ million. This price is based upon future land use as sub-divided real estate — but admittedly this is years away. The supply of such land for the future is scarce and the price today reflects it. The ranch will be sold at something near the asking price because the demand is there.

As the years roll by, all of us will have to ask ourselves what the price of living is, what we are willing to pay to enjoy what we have. The expense is huge but so is our ability to enjoy what we have.

Can you imagine a world without a place for solitude? A place with no beauty? Not to have these things is the highest price we could possibly pay.

September, 1972

"...his bill can hold more than his belican."

PELICANS HERE AND NOW

Recently, while beaching and playing tennis in Florida, I watched several flocks of from four to eleven brown pelicans sail by, occasionally giving some slow strong beats with their wings, and I wondered why we have so few pelicans in Minnesota.

Pelicans in Minnesota, you say? Definitely, yes. Apparently we have only the white pelican but that should be enough, because it is the largest bird found in our state with a length of name to match its size — *Pelecanus erythrorhynchos*. It is not only the largest bird in Minnesota but is huge in its own right. It varies from five to six feet in length and some have a wingspread of nearly nine feet. They weigh about sixteen pounds.

I have three memories of experiences with pelicans in Minnesota. One of them is an indirect one when I was reading a book of Ogden Nash's poems many years ago, but I've never forgotten his verse about the pelican — "his bill can hold more than his belican."

A second memory is a direct one that happened way back in the mid-30s. I can close my eyes and see the scene exactly. I was standing on the west shore of Farm Island Lake south of Aitkin, Minnesota on a dull, gray day in late summer, the wind was blowing from the south and the water had quite a chop to it. Out of the north and into the wind came a flock of the largest and whitest birds I had ever seen. They coasted down and landed in front of me — all thirty or forty of them. There was no mistake that they were white pelicans, not only because of their size, but also because of the massive yellow pouches under their bills. How could any boy forget a sight like that?

A third experience occurred not too many years ago on the shore of Lake Minnetonka. I was standing on my north lawn at the Pass waiting to be picked up by a friend to go duck-hunting when a single, magnificent, immense, white creature of a pelican came from the west across Halsteds Bay, right over my head, flying not more than twenty-five feet above the ground, and landed in the Upper Lake by Wawatosa Island. It stayed there for ten minutes or so before it took off to the southeast, passing over Smithtown Bay. For the record, this bird flew by at 1:30 p.m., Friday, October 6, 1967. This may seem late in the season, but I checked Robert's *Birds of Minnesota* and his latest recorded date of a white pelican in Minnesota is listed as October 3, 1907, on Heron Lake in Jackson County.

Pelicans used to be very common in Minnesota and were regular spring and fall visitors to Lake Minnetonka before the turn of the century. The Ojibway Indians called the pelican the *shetek* and Pelican Lake in Grant County used to be named Lake Shetek. In the "Song of Hiawatha," Longfellow used the name *shada* when referring to the pelican. In Minnesota, we have Pelican Rapids, several Pelican Lakes, Little Pelican Lake, Pelican River, Pelican Creek, Pelican Township, and near Brown's Valley, a Pelican Hill. There are Pelican lakes in Manitoba, Nebraska, Saskatchewan, Wisconsin, and Florida, in addition to Minnesota.

Why don't we have numerous pelicans today in our state? I don't know. They eat only fish and seem to get along with people, and the changes in our state since seventy or eighty years ago shouldn't necessarily discourage their existence. (Since this column was printed in 1972, numerous reports have substantiated pelicans being regular visitors today.)

Pelicans are old birds in relation to geologic time. They evolved over 50 million years ago and are on their way out,

White Pelican

along with most other birds not of the perching bird or
Passerine order. They migrate each year (at least the white
ones do) and even Aristotle, when writing on bird migration,
stated, "Pelicans also migrate and fly from Strynon to the
Ister." I have to assume the pelicans knew what he meant,
although I don't.

White pelicans are slow flyers, beating their wings about
1.3 times per second. This compares to a hummingbird's
70 times per second. Unlike the brown pelican who dives
for its food, the white pelican flaps its wings over or on the
water and creates a big commotion to drive small fish into
the shallows. He then scoops them up with the bill and large
pouch. Some gulls steal fish from the pouch as the pelican
is waiting for the water to drain out before eating the fish.
The young of the pelican spend their early days eating only

regurgitated food from the parent, consuming as much as 150 pounds before being mature enough to seek their own food.

Pelicans are great soarers because of their big wings, and it's a graceful group that glides the beaches. With a moderate wind they can soar for miles, but I've noticed that when the leader of a formation beats his wings, they all have to. Apparently, his wing beats disrupt their air currents and the soaring is disturbed. None of them seem to beat their wings until the leader does, in sort of a follow-the-leader routine.

I hope the white pelican can make a comeback in our Minnesota state, as well as elsewhere. Those of you who have never seen this bird have missed a great thrill. The state of Louisiana has made the pelican its state bird, but for some strange reason the official bird is the brown pelican, while a white pelican is on the state flag.

If anybody has seen white pelicans in Minnesota in the past, or if you see them in the future, please document the sighting and report it to the Museum of Natural History at the University of Minnesota, the Sun newspaper, or the Department of Natural Resources, State of Minnesota. Look sharp. It's always possible one or more will come winging their way your way. Lucky you.

November, 1972

*"...the subject aged, the pendulum started
to return in its back swing, and finally settled
into a position somewhere in the middle."*

CONSERVATIVE CONSERVATION

Recently, I gave a speech at the Wayzata, Minnesota, Universalist-Unitarian Church. I have spoken there once before and the topic then was my usual one regarding the need for freshwater knowledge, the need for freshwater scientists, and the need for the Freshwater Biological Institute. This time, the topic was "Conservative Conservation."

Conservation is no different from other things in that it, too, has its pros and cons, its extremists and its ultra-conservatives. Conservation and ecology, other environmental aspects of our life, and things around us have gone through the normal swing of the pendulum that happens to all of those factors that have major effects upon our lives. Unionism, liberalism, bossism, isolationism, and such burst upon the public at one time or another, interest became intense, reactions and counter-reactions caused the pendulum of public pressure to swing high, wide and handsome in one direction. Then as the subject aged, the pendulum started to return in its back swing, and finally settled into a position somewhere in the middle.

So it is today with the environmental movement. It was only three years ago (in 1969) that an ecological conscience was born within the general public in the United States (if not in the world) and the bandwagon was overcrowded with those steeped in the new interest. That phase is now over, I feel, and the pendulum is now falling back from its peak swing position that was reached sometime during 1971. And in my opinion, that's good.

I feel it's good because too many things were happening in the name of conservation and ecology without adequate knowledge, without good reasons or, at least, without giving the "heat of battle" time to cool down.

A beautiful lesson in grass-roots and down-to-earth conservation is presented in a marvelous three-part article in the *New Yorker* magazine, entitled "The Tree Where Man was Born" by Peter Matthiessen. I heartily recommend these articles because the rawness, the life and death, the tragedies of nature's own way of practicing conservation are presented in straightforward, stark language that strikes home. The articles are in the 1972 issues of September 16, 23, and 30. (Possibly they're now in book form.)

The delicate balance between the natural and what man can do to upset this balance is illustrated by a small happening to the author of these articles. He was observing the calving of a herd of wildebeest on the plains of East Africa and noted that a young calf will imprint on the nearest moving thing to it at birth. He was being careful not to get too close to the herd. One time, however, a newborn calf followed him from the grazing herd and his efforts to lead the calf back to the herd resulted in the herd being put to flight. The calf couldn't follow the herd, the herd forsook it, and the calf wouldn't allow itself to be caught. He writes, "Finally, I, too, left it behind. A mile away, I could still see it (I can see it to this day) — a thin, still thing come to a halt at last on the silent plain." It breaks your heart.

To practice conservation and all of its ramifications, we must know what we're doing. In my opinion, this leaves no room for the extremist who obstructs rather than instructs, who balks unintelligently instead of talking intelligently. Too many have come forward unprepared or wishing to take the stand just for the sake of being heard, having nothing to contribute but the negative.

The great danger of high pendulum swings of any

The gradual destroying of a portion of forest by an act of man

movement is the backlash that may happen. I hope it's not happening to the ecological-conservation movement. Recently, a lot of people have stated to me how silly they think total burning-ban ordinances are, for example, and by golly they're going to burn their leaves this fall. A mild backlash, but one that's in existence.

I just hope that from now on conservation can be practiced in a conservative way, not ultra-conservative, but instead in a middle-of-the-road way. I'm the first to admit that there will be delays while searching for the proper way, that there will be instances where possibly prompt or immediate action should be taken. But, in general, what is trying to be done will have long-range effects on our lives and we must be sure we're right in what we're doing. In the meantime, we wish to continue to live.

Two weeks ago, I stood on a platform in Nashwauk, Minnesota, looking down on a closed open-pit iron ore mine of the Hanna Mining Company. Twenty-five million tons of iron ore had been removed from this pit of earth before 1962, and the deep water-filled pit with sheer sides and mountains of overburden cast aside during the mining remains as mute evidence of what man has asked for in the past. I say "asked for" because this is true. The public demanded steel and more steel and Hanna complied. The public created the open-pit mine. Without intending to take sides, I say that the Reserve Mining Company, as are other mining companies, is pressured by steel demand to extract more and more taconite; that Reserve was allowed to build the Silver Bay plant; and, right or wrong, we, as a consuming society, must work with Reserve for a reasonable time until a better solution is found, if possible. To a certain extent, the public has created the tailings going into Lake Superior at the rate of 67,000 tons daily.

Dozens of such examples can be cited, and all of them take place because the public wanted something and demanded something without realizing the consequences. The problems were created through lack of knowledge but with good intentions. The smog gets worse in Los Angeles, but cars are still allowed in ever-increasing numbers on the freeways with only one person in each car most of the time.

We have to tackle our environmental problems, and we have to practice proper and sane conservation, but I hope we can do it with intelligence, with caution but with haste, keeping our cool but still keeping the heat on. I call it conservative conservation.

October, 1972

Index